1976

University of St. Francis
GEN   581.133 S966
Sutcliffe
Mineral salts absorption in pl...

C0-AWE-945

INTERNATIONAL SERIES OF MONOGRAPHS ON
PURE AND APPLIED BIOLOGY

Division: **PLANT PHYSIOLOGY**

GENERAL EDITORS: P. F. WAREING and A. W. GALSTON

VOLUME 1

MINERAL SALTS ABSORPTION IN PLANTS

MINERAL SALTS ABSORPTION IN PLANTS

by

J. F. SUTCLIFFE, D.Sc.

Reader in Botany
King's College
University of London

LIBRARY
College of St. Francis
JOLIET, ILL.

PERGAMON PRESS

NEW YORK - OXFORD - LONDON - PARIS

1962

PERGAMON PRESS INC.
122 East 55th Street, New York 22, N.Y.
1404 New York Avenue, N.W., Washington 5, D.C.

PERGAMON PRESS LTD.
Headington Hill Hall, Oxford
4 & 5 Fitzroy Square, London W.1

PERGAMON PRESS S.A.R.L.
24 Rue des Écoles, Paris V

PERGAMON PRESS G.m.b.H.
Kaiserstrasse 75, Frankfurt am Main

Copyright © 1962
PERGAMON PRESS LTD

Library of Congress Card Number 61-18329

Set in Times New Roman and printed in Great Britain by
THE VILLAFIELD PRESS, BISHOPBRIGGS, GLASGOW

581.133
8966

73729

TO MY PARENTS
WITH LOVE AND IN GRATITUDE

PREFACE

THE variety of mineral salts which plants require for growth are taken up from the soil, or in the case of some aquatic plants, from the surrounding water. The mechanism of absorption has been extensively investigated during the past 30 years, and although it cannot be said that the process is entirely understood, much information has been obtained. This monograph is an attempt to summarize present knowledge and ideas for the benefit of students and research workers in the field of mineral nutrition.

The subject is discussed against its historical background (Chapter 1), proceeding from an account of experimental materials and methods (Chapter 2) to a description of the physico-chemical processes by which ions move in non-living systems (Chapter 3). A summary of the effects of various external and inherent factors on the course of absorption (Chapter 4) is followed by a consideration of the relationship between uptake and metabolism (Chapter 5). The location of accumulation mechanisms in cells is discussed in Chapter 6, and this leads to an account of salt absorption and transport in vascular plants (Chapter 7). Finally, there is a brief description of the soil as a source of mineral nutrients (Chapter 8) and a discussion of the physiology of salt tolerance (Chapter 9).

My heartfelt thanks are due to Professor T. A. Bennet-Clark, F.R.S., who has given me unstinted advice and encouragement in my investigations of salt absorption during the past 10 years. He read a draft of the manuscript for this book and made valuable suggestions for its improvement. The blame for any deficiencies or errors that remain is of course entirely my own. My thanks are also due to Professor F. C. Steward, F.R.S., for the benefit of many stimulating discussions during my tenure of a Rockefeller Foundation Fellowship at Cornell University in 1956–57, when many of the data upon which the text is based were compiled. I am grateful to Mrs. D. Howarth for her care in typing the manuscript, and to my wife, Janet, for assistance in the preparation

vii

of diagrams and the compilation of the bibliography and index. Finally, I wish to express my thanks to the Editors of the *International Series of Monographs*, and to Pergamon Press, for inviting me to prepare this volume, and for the assistance and co-operation, I have received from them in this task.

King's College,
London.

CONTENTS

When a plant is burned it is reduced to a salty ash called alcaly by apothecaries and philosophers . . . Every sort of plant without exception contains some kind of salt. Have you not seen certain labourers when sowing a field with wheat for the second year in succession burn the unused wheat straw which had been taken from the field? In the ashes will be found the salt that the straw took out of the soil; if it is put back the soil is improved. Being burnt on the ground it serves as manure because it returns to the soil those substances that had been taken away.

B. Palissy (1563)

CHAPTER 1

INTRODUCTION

A rational system of agriculture must be based on an
exact acquaintance with the means of nutrition of
vegetables, and with the influence of soils and action
of manure upon them.

LIEBIG (1840)

A. HISTORICAL

THE FACT that calcined plants yield an ash containing inorganic
salts has been known since antiquity, and the beneficial effect on
crops of adding this ash to soil was recognized in early agricultural
practice (see opposite). Nevertheless, the origin and significance of
the mineral elements in plants for long remained a matter of
controversy, and, as recently as the nineteenth century, it was still
being argued with some conviction that salts are created *de novo*
within them as a by-product of growth.

The classical experiment of Van Helmont (1577–1644), reported
by his son in *Ortus Medicinae* (1684) was the first quantitative
investigation of plant nutrition of which there is any record. He
planted a willow (*Salix* sp.) cutting, weighing 5 lb, in 200 lb of dry
earth, and watered it with rain-water over a period of 5 years. At
the end, the plant weighed 169 lb 3 oz, and the earth had lost about
2 oz in dry weight. The experiment successfully disproved Aristotle's
view that plants absorb their food in an elaborated form from the
soil (humus theory), but Van Helmont concluded, perhaps under-
standably in the existing state of knowledge, that 164 lb of plant
material had been produced from water alone. He did not enlarge
on the significance of the small decrease in dry weight of the soil,
which was presumably due to removal of inorganic substances.
Woodward (1699) pointed out that plants can survive with their
roots immersed in water, but growth is better in river water than in
rain-water, and best in a watery extract of soil (Table 1). On the

1

basis of these observations, he disputed Van Helmont's conclusion, and asserted that "earth, and not water, is the matter that constitutes vegetables."

Although Hales (*Vegetable Staticks*, 1727) perceived that plants are nourished in part from the air through the leaves, it was not until the nineteenth century that a proper distinction was made between photosynthesis and mineral nutrition. De Saussure (*Recherches chimiques sur la Végétation*, 1804) maintained that the soil supplies a small but essential part of plant nutrients, including nitrogen and

TABLE 1. GROWTH OF MINT PLANTS IN WATER FROM
VARIOUS SOURCES
(Woodward, 1699)

Source of water	Initial wt. of plants (grains)	Gain in wt. in 77 days (grains)
Rain	28·25	17·5
River Thames	28·0	26·0
Hyde Park conduit	110·0	139·0
Hyde Park conduit (garden mould added)	92·0	284·0

mineral elements. He showed that if a plant is grown from seed in water alone, there is no gain in ash except for the relatively small increment which may result from deposition of dust. In spite of his clear experimental results and logical arguments, De Saussure's ideas did not receive immediate acceptance, nor were his quantitative methods of investigation adopted generally until more than 50 years later. The view that inorganic substances are mere accidental inclusions in plants, or at best mysterious "stimulants" rather than nutrients, was finally discarded following trenchant criticism by the chemist Liebig, in a famous address to the British Association for the Advancement of Science (*Die organische Chemie in ihrer Anwendung auf Agricultur und Physiologie*, 1840). The difficult problem of the sources of nitrogen for plants gave rise to much discussion towards the middle of the last century. Liebig maintained that gaseous nitrogen is not utilized and that the element is probably obtained by plants as ammonia from its surroundings. In 1856, he showed that nitrate is formed from nitrogenous fertilizers in soil, but it was not until 10 years later that the importance of nitrate as a plant nutrient was generally accepted. With this advance, the role of the soil as a source of inorganic salts for plants was firmly established.

B. SALT CONTENT OF PLANTS

The results of an ash analysis of a *Zea mays* plant are shown in Table 2. It can be seen that the elements present, excluding carbon,

TABLE 2. MINERAL CONTENT OF A *Zea mays* (PRIDE OF SALINE) PLANT GROWN AT MANHATTAN, KANSAS, IN 1920
(From Miller, 1938)

Element	Weight (g)	% of total dry weight
Nitrogen	12·2	1·46
Silicon	9·8	1·17
Potassium	7·7	0·92
Calcium	1·9	0·23
Phosphorus	1·7	0·20
Magnesium	1·5	0·18
Sulphur	1·4	0·17
Chlorine	1·2	0·14
Aluminium	0·9	0·11
Iron	0·7	0·08
Manganese	0·3	0·04
Undetermined	7·8	0·93
Total	47·1	5·63

hydrogen and oxygen, comprise a rather small percentage of the total dry weight, and more than half of this is made up of nitrogen, silicon and potassium. Most of the nitrogen and phosphorus in plants is present in organic compounds, while some of the other elements occur partly in this form. The bulk of each metallic element, however, exists as inorganic compounds or ions, and much of it is dissolved in the aqueous sap of cell vacuoles.

Plants are invariably rich in potassium, and the name, derived from "pot-ashes", commemorates an early method of preparing potassium salts. In contrast, aluminium is found in relatively small amounts in many plants, although it is an abundant constituent of soil. A few species contain large amounts of this element, notably the club mosses (*Lycopodium* spp.) and some members of the family *Diapensiaceae*, from which derives the importance of certain of these plants as sources of mordants for dyeing. Selenium is an element which is absorbed to widely different extents by different plants (Table 3). Some species of *Astragalus* growing on seleniferous

TABLE 3. AMOUNTS OF SELENIUM ABSORBED BY VARIOUS PLANTS FROM SOIL TO WHICH SODIUM SELENATE WAS ADDED AT A CONCENTRATION OF 5 PARTS PER MILLION
(Hurd-Karrer, 1935)

Plant	Selenium content (parts per million of dry weight)	Plant	Selenium content (parts per million of dry weight)
Brome grass	200	Pea	560
Maize (corn)	275	Sweet clover	645
Spinach	315	Flax	685
Barley	450	Sunflower	790
Wheat	470	Broccoli	1180
Oat	535	Mustard	1240

soils accumulate so much of it that animals eating them suffer from selenium poisoning ("alkali disease"). Strontium is absorbed to an appreciable extent by a number of plants, and may comprise 2–3 per cent of the total dry weight in exceptional cases. Crops which accumulate large amounts of strontium are a potential health hazard, since ^{90}Sr is a dangerous radioactive isotope, produced in nuclear explosions, which, if deposited in the bones of animals may induce leukaemia.

The accumulation of iodine by seaweeds has been well known since the element was discovered (in kelp) by Courtois in 1812. *Laminaria digitata* accumulates iodine to a concentration of about 3000 parts per million of water, from a concentration of less than 1 part per million in the sea. Bromine, too, is taken up by seaweeds, but it usually attains a somewhat lower concentration than iodine, in spite of the fact that its concentration in sea water is appreciably greater. A number of rare elements are accumulated to varying extents by seaweeds; titanium, for example, is concentrated 10,000-fold by *Fucus spiralis*, and 120-fold by *Laminaria digitata*. Altogether about sixty elements have been detected in plants, and the list will undoubtedly be extended as more sensitive methods of detection become available. A plant probably contains at least traces of all the elements present in the environment in which it grows. Absorption is not restricted to those which occur naturally; it has been shown, for example, that plants will readily take up plutonium which is produced artificially in nuclear reactors.

TABLE 4. COMPOSITION (MILLIEQUIVALENTS PER LITRE) OF THE SAP IN *Chara ceratophylla*, AND OF THE MEDIA IN WHICH THE PLANTS WERE GROWN (Collander, 1942)

	Na	K	Mg	Ca	Cl
Sap	152	66	26	13	233
Medium	68	1·4	14	3·8	80
Sap	126	61	20	11	208
Medium	31	0·6	6·5	2·0	36
Sap	84	77		13	176
Medium	0·21	0·04		3·3	0·13

Individual plant species tend to have a characteristic salt content, which is relatively independent of the composition of the medium in which they are grown—at least as far as physiologically important elements are concerned. Table 4 shows that the concentrations of salts present in the water in which the stonewort, *Chara ceratophylla* grows has little influence on the potassium, magnesium, or calcium content of the plant, although there are effects on the amounts of sodium and chloride taken up. The shoots of higher plants tend to show greater independence in this respect than do roots. In particular, sodium is present at a low concentration in the above-ground parts of many plants, irrespective of the amount of sodium in the soil, and it is for this reason that the diet of domestic animals (and man) which feed largely on shoots, must be supplemented with common salt.

C. FUNCTIONS OF MINERAL SALTS

The presence of a particular element in a plant does not necessarily imply that it serves a useful function there. In order to prove that an element is essential, it is necessary to show that symptoms of malnutrition become visible in its absence which can be corrected by supplying that element, and in no other way. The procedure for testing indispensability usually involves growing plants from seed in solutions lacking the element and comparing them with others grown in a complete medium. Using the technique of "solution" or "water" culture, it was established by Sachs, Knop and other late nineteenth-century investigators, that, in addition to carbon, hydrogen and oxygen, seven elements are universally essential for plant growth. These are *nitrogen, phosphorus, sulphur, potassium, calcium, magnesium* and *iron*. This list differs in only one respect from that compiled by De Saussure in 1804, namely in the substitution of iron for silicon.

Since the time of these early investigations, further research along similar lines, employing highly purified chemicals and more refined techniques, has established that at least six other elements are required in small amounts by some, and probably by all, plants. These, together with iron, are the so-called "micronutrients" or "trace elements" and they include *boron, chlorine, copper, manganese molybdenum* and *zinc* (Table 5). In the absence of a sufficient

TABLE 5. A LIST OF THE ESSENTIAL ELEMENTS OF PLANTS, AND THE FORMS IN WHICH THEY ARE MAINLY ABSORBED
Non-ionic sources in brackets

MACRONUTRIENTS		MICRONUTRIENTS	
Carbon	(Carbon dioxide)	Boron	Borates
	Bicarbonate	Chlorine	Chloride
Hydrogen	(Water)	Copper	Cations
	Various anions	Iron	Cations
Oxygen	(Water, gaseous oxygen)	Manganese	Cations
	Various anions		Manganates
Nitrogen	Nitrate, ammonium	Molybdenum	Molybdates
Phosphorus	Phosphates	Zinc	Cations
Sulphur	Sulphates		
Potassium	Cations		
Calcium	Cations		
Magnesium	Cations		

amount of any one of these elements distinctive symptoms of malnutrition become visible, which are sometimes referred to as "deficiency diseases", and which can be corrected by supplying the missing nutrient.

There are indications that various elements, in addition to those which are known to be essential, are beneficial to the growth of many plants, and may be indispensable for some. Those elements to which particular attention has been directed include *cobalt, silicon, sodium* and *vanadium*. *Cobalt* is an essential element for animals, and various micro-organisms must be supplied with Vitamin B_{12} of which cobalt is a constituent. A small amount of cobalt is said to be required by blue-green algae, and the growth of higher plant cells is also affected by its absence. Early investigators established that *silicon* is not a major nutrient, but since it is extremely difficult to free solutions from the last traces of this element, evidence that it is not a micronutrient is still inconclusive. Silicon is certainly essential for the normal growth of those algae which possess silicious cell walls, but although it comprises a large part of the total ash in some monocotyledons (see Table 2), higher plants can apparently be grown in its virtual absence without ill effects. *Sodium* has often been found to promote the growth of plants under conditions of partial potassium deficiency, and this has led to the idea that sodium can substitute for potassium to some extent. An obligate requirement for both sodium and potassium has been claimed for some blue-green algae, and sodium cannot be replaced by any other element without detrimental effects on the growth of marine algae. *Vanadium* is apparently an essential element for the green alga, *Scenedesmus obliquus*, and it can replace molybdenum in some species of nitrogen-fixing bacteria (*Clostridium* spp.).

For optimum growth, the essential elements must be supplied in soluble form, and only at certain fairly definite concentrations. An excessive amount of one element, and particularly of a micro-nutrient, results in the appearance of toxicity symptoms. In the case of boron and copper, growth of many plants is inhibited when concentrations greater than 1 part per million are supplied, whereas deficiency symptoms develop at concentrations lower than about 0·05 parts per million. Chloride is the only micronutrient which can be presented to many plants at a relatively high concentration without ill effects (see Chapter 9).

The functions of most of the essential elements are well under-stood. *Nitrogen* and *sulphur*, for example, occur in proteins, and in many other cell constituents. *Phosphorus* enters into the composition of nucleic acids, phospholipids, and a number of coenzymes, including the pyridine nucleotides and nucleoside phosphates. Although *potassium* is required in considerable quantity for optimum growth, the reason for this remains largely obscure. It occurs mainly in ionic state in cell vacuoles, where it is generally the most abundant cation, and plays a major part in osmotic regulation. In this role it can be replaced at least partly by sodium or other easily absorbed cations. In addition, some potassium exists in bound forms in the cytoplasm where it assists in maintaining the unique structure and activity of protoplasm. It has been shown to activate a number of enzymes *in vitro*, but its importance as a natural enzyme activator is not yet certain.

The bulk of the *calcium* in plants occurs as calcium pectate in cell walls where it may assist in the regulation of growth. Calcium phosphatides are constituents of protoplasmic membranes and may exert an important influence on their properties. Crystals of calcium oxalate are to be found in many cells, and a useful function of calcium may be to neutralize organic acids which might otherwise be toxic. Calcium ions become adsorbed by proteins and exert, in conjunction with other cations, a regulating influence on the hydration of cytoplasm. Some plants ("calcifuge" species) are usually confined to acid soils where the amount of calcium is low, while others ("calcicole" species) occur only in soils where calcium abounds. The basis of this distinction is probably complex, involving not only varying sensitivity to high and low calcium levels, but also interactions with other ions pH effects and competition between species. *Magnesium* is known to be the only metallic constituent of chlorophylls, and about 10 per cent of the magnesium in green tissues is incorporated in these pigments. In addition, magnesium is the normal activator of a number of important enzymes involved in respiration and photosynthesis.

Iron occurs in the prosthetic group of several respiratory enzymes, including the cytochromes, and in the ionic state, it activates several others. *Boron* is the one essential element for which no specific function is yet known. The other micronutrients are either constituents of enzymes, as in the case of *copper*, or serve as specific enzyme activators.

D. MECHANISM OF ABSORPTION

Recognition that mineral salts are absorbed and utilized by plants led naturally to speculation about the mechanism of uptake.

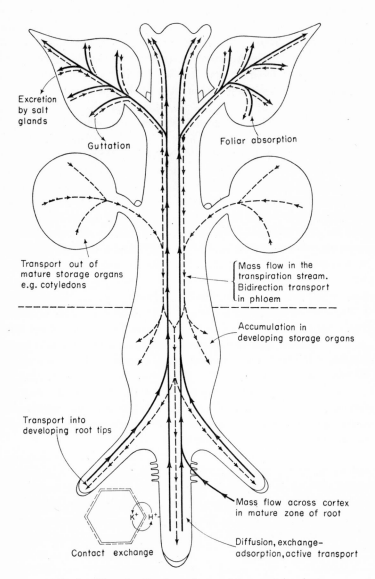

Fig. 1. Mineral salts absorption and transport in plants

An early idea was that salts were absorbed passively with the water that enters the plant. Such a view was expressed in Strasburger's well-known textbook and still finds some support today (see Chapter 7, pp. 116-7. A first indication of the inadequacy of this hypothesis came from observations of De Saussure that the salt composition of plants differs from that of the environment, and it became necessary to search for an alternative mechanism. The rapid increase in knowledge of physical chemistry during the nineteenth century provided a stimulus for most of the suggestions that were made. Mulder (*Physiologie Chemie*, 1851) argued for the importance of osmosis, that is, diffusion of substances across membranes in response to concentration gradients, pointing out that chemical transformation of particular molecules inside the protoplasm could result in continuous absorption, and also account for selectivity. This idea was supported by Sachs (1875) and Pfeffer (1900) who recognized, however, the inadequacy of diffusion and osmosis for transport of substances within plants at the rates observed. They emphasized the role of the transpiration stream in causing the rapid longitudinal movement of salts from roots to shoots.

The problem of the structure and properties of membranes, both living and non-living, began to interest physical chemists during the latter part of the nineteenth century. Traube (1867) suggested that membranes contain pores of fixed sizes through which molecules may pass if their dimensions are not too great (molecular sieve hypothesis). Overton (1895) on the other hand, demonstrated the importance of lipid solubility in determining the rate at which substances are transferred across membranes (lipid hypothesis). At first, the permeability of cytoplasm was looked upon as a passive property, comparable to that of non-living membranes, but Overton realised that the metabolism of the cell might play some part ("adenoid activity"). With remarkable insight, Pfeffer (1900) asserted that living organisms may possess the ability to transport substances across membranes in a particular direction, and to induce movement from cell to cell, in the absence of concentration gradients. He suggested that chemical combination with cell constituents may be involved in these processes, and thus conceived the idea of "carrier molecules" which is now in vogue.

Pfeffer's suggestion was received without enthusiasm, and for many years afterwards physical mechanisms were continually emphasized. It was gradually realized that since those salts which are absorbed by plants are dissociated in aqueous solution, the problem is primarily one of ionic, rather than molecular transport. In the early years of the present century, the unequal uptake of the two ions of a single salt was demonstrated both with isolated tissues (Meurer, 1909; Ruhland, 1909), and whole plants (Pantanelli, 1915). Attempts were made to explain these observations in terms of the establishment of Donnan equilibria, adsorption and ion exchange.

In the decade from about 1930, it was clearly established, mainly through the investigations of Hoagland in the United States of America, Lundegårdh in Sweden, and Steward in England, that salt uptake depends largely on aerobic metabolism. This led to speculation concerning the relationship between absorption and

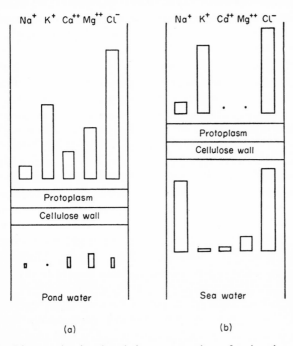

(a)   (b)

Fig. 2.   Diagram showing the relative concentrations of various ions in the sap of *Nitella clavata* (a), and *Valonia macrophysa* (b); and in the medium in which the plants were grown. The vertical scale of (a) $\frac{1}{10}$ is that of (b).
Redrawn from Hoagland (1944)

respiration, and schemes linking the physical processes of diffusion, adsorption and exchange to metabolism were proposed. Analyses of sap from vacuoles (see p. 19), showed unequivocally for the first time that both cations and anions can be accumulated by plants against existing concentrating gradients (Fig. 2, cf. Table 4 p. 5) and confirmed the inadequacy of purely physical mechanisms. In spite of extensive investigations, the manner in which respiration participates in the absorption of salt is still far from clear, as the subsequent discussion will show.

The study of metabolically-mediated ion transport, or "active transport" as it is often called, has gained a much wider biological importance since its first recognition in plants. Active transport also occurs in animals, where it is involved in the contraction of muscle, transmission of nerve impulses, and regulation of the ionic composition of erythrocytes, body fluids and urine. In animals, an ionic balance is usually established within cells and tissues, whereas in plants the prominent feature is accumulation of salts by growing organisms without the establishment of equilibria. Elucidation of the basic mechanisms of ion transport in biological systems remains one of the most challenging problems to both animal and plant physiologists.

For further reading

GAMBLE, J. L. (1947). *Chemical Anatomy, Physiology and Pathology of Extracellular Fluids.* Harvard University Press, Cambridge, Mass.

MULDER, E. G. (1950). Mineral nutrition of plants. *Ann. Rev. Plant Physiol.* **1**, 1–24.

REED, H. S. (1942). Plant Nutrition. In *A Short History of the Plant Sciences.* Chap. 16, pp. 241–53. Chronica Botanica, Waltham, Mass.

SACHS, J. von (1890). *History of the theory of the nutrition of plants.* (Chap. 2, pp. 445–534). (Translated by H. E. F. Garnsey and revised by I. B. Balfour.) Book III, in *History of Botany* (1530–1860).

CHAPTER 2

EXPERIMENTAL MATERIALS
AND METHODS

The methods in physiology are in no respect different
from those employed in other sciences, and thus in
order to obtain a sufficiently broad comprehension
of the phenomena observed, and to permit the
establishment of general laws, it is essential that a
comparative study of a great variety of plants should
be made.

W. PFEFFER. *The Physiology of Plants* (1900)

A. EXPERIMENTAL MATERIALS

1. *Intact Angiosperms*

Salt absorption has been studied in a wide variety of botanical
materials, ranging from intact angiosperms rooted in soil to sub-
cellular organelles. The earliest investigations were conducted upon
whole vascular plants growing under natural conditions, but now-
adays most plant physiologists have abandoned soil to the soil
scientists, and have chosen to concentrate their efforts on elucidating
the lesser (but still considerable) complexities presented by plants
growing in solution culture. Many have taken a step further and
regard an intact angiosperm as too complicated a system for useful
investigation. Instead, isolated parts of plants are used as experimental material, with the ultimate objective of building up an
integrated picture of salt absorption and transport in the whole
organism. Much can be learned about the mechanism of ion
movements at the cell level by the study of homogenous tissues, but
the relevance of such knowledge to the processes going on in the
intact plant must ultimately be demonstrated rather than assumed.

2. *Excised Roots*

Many investigators have favoured the use of excised roots in the

13

study of salt uptake, because roots are the major absorbing organs in most angiosperms. The system is less complex than is a whole plant, inasmuch as any influences of the shoot on uptake by the root are removed, and it is somewhat less variable in behaviour. The material is usually prepared by growing plants (barley, *Hordeum vulgare*, and wheat, *Triticum* spp., have often been used) in media containing a low concentration of salts for several days, under uniform conditions of light and temperature. The "low salt" roots so obtained have a high sugar content, and after excision are capable of absorbing salt rapidly for a limited time, in a reproducible manner.

Various objections can be raised to the claim that excised roots are ideal material for salt absorption studies:

(a) The shoot may exert an important influence on absorption by roots, e.g. by virtue of transpiration, and this obviously cannot be investigated adequately in excised roots.

(b) When roots are separated from the rest of the plant in the manner normally employed for salt absorption studies, they rapidly stop growing and are clearly in an abnormal physiological state which may well affect the uptake process. Techniques are now available (White, 1954) for culturing excised roots in nutrient media in such a way that they continue to grow, more or less normally, but these have not yet been applied extensively to investigations of salt uptake.

(c) Excised roots are not much less complex structurally than is an entire plant, and results obtained from experiments with them are thus difficult to interpret at the cell level. Absorption occurs simultaneously into a heterogeneous mixture of meristematic, expanding and mature cells, and in addition there is transport across the cortex into the stele (Fig. 3). When the roots are entirely immersed in a solution, the possibility exists that salts absorbed from the medium are released again from the cut ends of the xylem vessels, so that the true rate of absorption may be difficult to ascertain. Unfortunately, many investigators have attempted to interpret their observations as if the organ consisted of a homogeneous mass of parenchyma, and have ignored its manifest complexity.

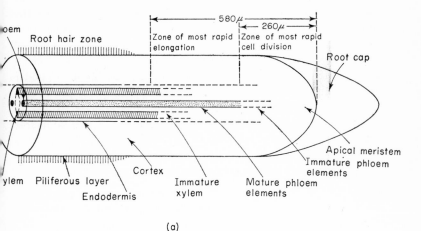

(a)

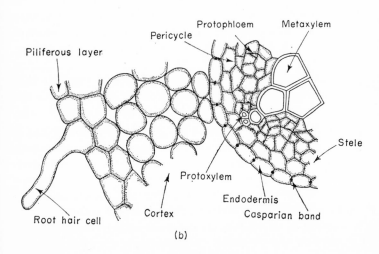

(b)

Fig. 3. Root Anatomy.

a. Diagram of a tobacco root tip showing the spatial relations of different tissues and order of maturation (redrawn from Esau, 1953); b. Transverse section of a root (after Priestley, 1920)

Details of a successful method of preparing excised roots for salt absorption studies were given by Hoagland and Broyer (1936), and this technique with variations has been employed in a number of more recent investigations.

3. *Slices of Storage Tissues*

De Vries (1871) used thin sections of red beet (*Beta vulgaris*) in an investigation of the permeability of plasmolysed protoplasts, but Nathanson (1904) and Meurer (1909) were perhaps the earliest investigators to employ storage tissue parenchyma on a large scale in absorption studies, and to point out its advantages. The material

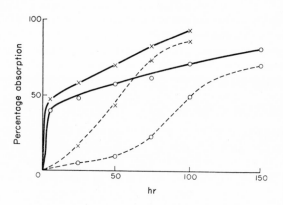

FIG. 4.   Absorption of manganese (—) and chloride (---) from a solutiorn of manganese chloride (0·001M) by parsnip tissue washed for either 24 hr (o) or 168 hr (x) in aerated distilled water (redrawn from Rees, 1949)

is readily available in bulk, is easily prepared, and under suitable conditions takes up salts readily. Storage organs which have been widely used include potato (*Solanum tuberosum*) and artichoke (*Helianthus tuberosus*) tubers; turnip and swede (*Brassica rapa*) hypocotyls; red beet and carrot (*Daucus carota*) roots.

Freshly-cut slices of these tissues absorb salts slowly, but the cells become more active after washing for a time in aerated distilled water or dilute salt solution (Fig. 4). The fact that some tissues, e.g. the pulp of mature apple fruits, cannot be successfully reactivated in this way, merits further investigation. Steward (1937) emphasized that tissues capable of rapid salt absorption after washing are those which are able to synthesize protein and resume growth by callus formation at a cut surface.

In order to take full advantage of the homogeneity of the cells in storage tissues, the material is used in the form of thin disks, preferably not exceeding 1 mm in thickness. This minimizes any differences in absorption by cells at the surface and inside the slice, so that the experimental observations can be assumed to reflect the uniform behaviour of individual cells in the tissue as a whole.

Against the use of storage tissues, it has been argued that dormant organs consist of highly specialized cells, which do not normally regain a capacity to absorb salt once growth has stopped. The process of salt uptake induced in such cells may, therefore, bear little relation to that occurring in the roots of intact plants. There is, however, no evidence that this is the case, and it seems probable that a greater knowledge of the mechanism operative in tissue slices may assist in the elucidation of salt absorption in more complex systems (but see p. 13).

4. *Callus Tissue Cultures*

Although excised roots and storage tissue slices have an inherent capacity for growth,* this is not always manifested during an absorption experiment. With these materials, therefore, salt uptake can be studied without the complicating influence of concomitant growth. A study of salt absorption in non-growing tissues is, however, of limited interest, and should be supplemented with observations on growing cells, since growth has important effects on the absorption mechanism. Ideally, homogeneous populations of either actively-dividing or -expanding cells must be employed if experimental data are to be adequately interpreted at the cell level. As far as higher plants are concerned, an approach to these can be obtained through the technique of tissue culture.

Early methods of culturing tissues on the surface of agar proved unsuitable for most physiological studies because of the slow and variable growth induced. The discovery that uniform, rapidly growing cultures of carrot, and other storage tissue cells in liquid media can be obtained under the stimulus of growth-promoting

---

* Growth is defined in this context as increase in cell number, an irreversible increase in cell size, or net synthesis of protein.

factors in coconut milk (Steward and Shantz, 1956) has placed a new and valuable experimental material in the hands of plant physiologists. The tissue cultures, as grown at present, are not entirely satisfactory for investigations of salt absorption, because the gradual isolation of innermost cells from the medium as growth proceeds results in extensive differentiation. To avoid such difficulties attempts are being made to produce dispersed cultures of meristematic cells, preferably with synchronized divisions, which can be stimulated at will to pass into the vacuolated condition.

5. *Micro-organisms*

Unicellular algae, yeasts and bacteria can be grown relatively easily in pure culture under controlled conditions, and have been used extensively in the study of salt absorption. Investigations with these organisms might contribute greatly to a unified theory of salt accumulation in plants, if microbiologists and plant physiologists had greater liaison.

Advantages exhibited by micro-organisms over cells of higher plants for physiological investigations include:

(*a*) the more rapid rates of metabolism and growth;

(*b*) the relative ease with which cell division and enlargement can be distinguished in the growth of a population; and

(*c*) the wide range of conditions, e.g. of aeration and nutrient supply, under which growth occurs.

Micro-organisms have a less extensive vacuole system than is found in parenchyma cells of higher plants (Fig. 5), and one may therefore predict the existence of interesting differences between absorption mechanisms in the various cell types. Meristematic cells of higher plants may have more in common with micro-organisms than with parenchyma in this respect.

6. *Multicellular Algae*

The ability of multicellular algae to survive in sea-water has received considerable attention, as will be described in Chapter 9, and such studies may assist in solving some of the more general problems of salt absorption. Investigations have mainly been confined to species, such as *Ulva lactuca* and *Porphyra perforata*, which have thin flattened fronds, consisting of two layers of rather

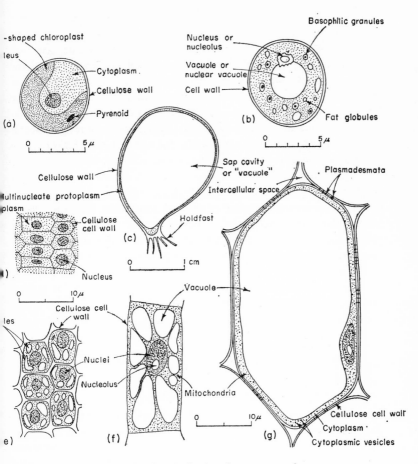

FIG. 5.   Drawings indicating the structure of:
a⊙A green alga (*Chlorella* sp.); b⊙A yeast cell; c⊙A coenocytic alga
(*Valonia* sp.); d—g. Stages in the development of vacuolated parenchyma

uniform cells. In such species, diffusion effects, which confuse the
situation in bulkier algae, are minimized.

7. *Coenocytes*

There are a number of non-cellular plants, classified among the
algae and fungi, which consist of either a single unit, or a number
of multinucleate units, called "coenocytes". Some of the coenocytic

algae, particularly *Valonia macrophysa, Valonia ventricosa* and *Halicystis* spp. which grow in warm seas, have attracted the attention of plant physiologists interested in salt accumulation. One reason for this is the relatively large size of coenocytes (a single coenocyte in *Valonia*, for example, may have a volume of several cm^2) which makes it possible for uncontaminated vacuolar sap to be extracted for detailed chemical analysis (Fig. 2, p. 11). Other manipulations are also feasible, which are impossible or difficult to accomplish with vacuolated cells; for example, separation of the cellulose wall from the protoplast is possible, and measurements of electrical potential differences and resistances between the medium and vacuolar sap can be made.

There is an unfortunate tendency among plant physiologists to homologize the structure of a coenocytic alga with that of a single vacuolated cell of higher plants and even to refer to a coenocyte as a "cell". In fact, coenocytes have probably arisen from multi-cellular tissues by disappearance of intervening walls, and are analogous rather than homologous with cells. In some genera of coenocytic algae, e.g. *Dictyosphaeria*, some of the cross walls are retained, dividing the protoplasm into multinucleate compartments across which salts are transferred in a manner reminiscent of secretion through multicellular membranes in animals. These remarks are not meant to imply that the mechanism of salt accumulation in the sap cavity of a coenocyte is necessarily different from that involved in parenchyma cells, but care should be taken when comparing observations made with the two kinds of material, and to avoid confusion, the correct nomenclature should be used.

8. *Mycelial Fungi*

The mechanism of salt uptake by fungal hyphae has hardly been studied, and an extensive investigation might profitably be undertaken with this material. The fact that the guttation fluid from *Pilobolus* sporangiophores contains salts at a high concentration suggests that fungi probably accumulate ions in the central cavity of the hyphae, where they assist in the maintenance of turgidity. It would be interesting to examine the extent to which the mechanism involved resembles that of accumulation in the vacuoles of parenchyma cells. Elucidation of the salt relations of fungi may improve our understanding of the manner in which the fungal component assists in the absorption of salt by mycorrhiza, a process which has already been investigated to some extent (Harley and McCready, 1950).

9. Leaves

Although terrestrial angiosperms absorb most of their mineral nutrients through the roots, a small amount is taken up via the leaves. The problem of foliar absorption is becoming increasingly important in agriculture and horticulture, and merits more attention from plant physiologists than it has yet received.

Aquatic angiosperms absorb salts mainly through the leaves, and the mechanism of uptake has been studied in such plants as *Elodea* (*Anacharis*) spp., *Lemna* spp., *Potomogeton* spp. and *Vallisneria* spp. Intact plants, segments of shoots bearing leaves, single leaves, and pieces of leaf have been used. Arisz (1953) devised a technique for measuring the rate of longitudinal translocation of chloride ions from one segment of a *Vallisneria* leaf to another. Transverse movement of calcium ions across leaves has been studied in *Potomogeton* and other aquatic plants, by using the leaf as a membrane separating two aqueous media (Arens, 1936, Steemann-Nielsen, 1951, Lowenhaupt, 1956).

10. Cell Organelles

It is generally assumed that the bulk of the salt absorbed by parenchyma cells is accumulated in *vacuoles*. In support of this view it has been observed that cells plasmolyzed in hypertonic salt solutions recover at a rate which is consistent with complete transfer of the absorbed ions into the central vacuole (Sutcliffe, 1954a). Isolated vacuoles have been obtained from *Allium* epidermal cells, and found to behave as osmometers (Chambers and Höfler, 1931; Vreugdenhil, 1957), but their ability to accumulate ions against a concentration gradient has not been demonstrated.

Intact *mitochondria* can now be isolated from plant cells, and their metabolic and osmotic properties have been studied *in vitro*. Following similar work on animal mitochondria, Robertson *et al* (1955) showed that mitochondria extracted from plants will accumulate salts by a mechanism which depends on metabolism. *Chloroplasts* and *nuclei* contain appreciable amounts of inorganic ions, mainly combined with organic substances, but as yet, the mechanism of salt absorption by these organelles has not been investigated. Further studies of ion uptake in biochemically-active preparations of sub-cellular particles will undoubtedly lead to a greater understanding of the process of absorption, and the spatial location of ion-transport mechanism in cells.

B. EXPERIMENTAL METHODS

1. *Qualitative Determinations*

The intake of salts by plant cells can sometimes be detected by microscopic observations, and various ingenious techniques were devised by early investigators for this purpose. One of the most successful of these methods involves measurement of the rate of recovery of a vacuolated cell after it has been plasmolysed in a hypertonic solution. If solute is absorbed, the osmotic pressure of the vacuolar sap gradually increases and its volume expands through the uptake of water. This procedure was used by De Vries (1871) in an attempt to demonstrate the penetration of sodium chloride into red beet cells.

Entry of coloured ions into cells can sometimes be followed by direct microscopic observation. If, however, the cell remains colourless upon immersion in a solution of dye, it is not certain, that the coloured ions have failed to enter because some dyes are decolourized at the redox potential of the cell. Penetration of colourless ions can occasionally be detected as a result of formation of coloured complexes with cell constituents; iron, for example, gives a blue coloration in the presence of tannins. Alternatively, microchemical tests can be applied to show the presence of certain ions in cells following immersion of a tissue in salt solutions. Diphenylamine has been used in this way to demonstrate uptake of nitrate. If a cell contains soluble carbonates or oxalates, absorption of calcium ions is indicated by the appearance of crystals of insoluble calcium salts.

More recently, the technique of autoradiography has been used to show the uptake by root tips of such ions as phosphate and sulphate, labelled with radioactive isotopes and even to demonstrate their intracellular location (Howard and Pelc, 1951).

2. Quantitative Determinations

a. General. Absorption of salts by whole plants, or their parts, can be determined quantitatively by analysis of samples of either the medium or the tissue, before and after a period of uptake. In practice, analysis of the medium is often preferred, since it is then possible to measure absorption after several consecutive time intervals with the same plant material. Moreover, analysis of the tissue is often less reliable than that of the medium owing to the presence of a greater number of substances, which may interfere with the determination, and difficulty may be encountered in extracting salt quantitatively, especially if some has been incorporated into organic cell constituents.

If a tissue contains initially an appreciable amount of the salt under investigation, the change in concentration as a result of absorption may be smaller, and less easily determined with accuracy, than are the concomitant changes in composition of the medium. On the other hand, if the volume of medium is large relative to the volume of tissue, and the concentration of salt is high, the reverse may be true, and an analysis of the tissue may be preferred. In general, the most satisfactory experiments are those in which it is possible to analyse the medium at intervals, and then confirm the total amount of salt absorbed by a final analysis of the tissue.

b. Methods of analysis.

i. *Chemical analysis.* Quantitative macro- and micro-analytical methods are available for determining the amounts of the most important elements taken up by plants (see Humphries, 1956a). Although these methods are accurate, they are frequently laborious, and are often replaced by more convenient physical methods, when such are available.

ii. *Physical methods. a. Conductivity determinations.* A change in the total concentration of ions in a solution can be estimated from the change in electrical conductivity. It must be noted, however, that if uptake of one ion is accompanied by release into the medium of a different ion with the same electrical charge, little or no change in conductivity may be detected even though an appreciable amount of a particular ion may have been removed from the solution.

β. *Polarography* has been successfully used for the determination of a variety of ions. For details of the technique, particularly as applied to analyses of plant materials, see Riches (1948).

c. *Flame photometry* has gained widespread popularity for the estimation of some cations, particularly sodium and potassium ions. The apparatus required is inexpensive, while the method is rapid and reasonably accurate. An aqueous solution of salt is injected into an air–coal gas, or air–butane, flame under controlled conditions and the intensity of radiation at a selected wavelength is determined photometrically. With the assistance of calibration curves based on analyses of solutions of known concentration, the amount of salt in an unknown solution can be measured. Selective optical filters are available which enable determinations of one ion to be made in the presence of another, for example potassium can be estimated in presence of sodium, and vice versa. The flame spectrophotometer is a more elaborate instrument than the flame photometer, incorporating a monochromator, and exhibiting greater sensitivity and versatility.

d. *Radioactive isotopes.* The availability of a variety of radioactive isotopes since about 1945 has made possible the introduction of a new and powerful technique for the measurement of ion movements. Some of the isotopes which have been used are listed in Table 6. Gamma-radiation easily penetrates a thin layer of glass and counters, incorporating a Geiger-Müller (G.M) tube within a glass envelope have been designed for measuring the radioactivity of labelled salt solutions. Beta-radiation, which does not penetrate glass to an appreciable extent, is usually measured by means of an end-window, G.M tube, in conjunction with electronic counting equipment. An aliquot of the radioactive solution or tissue extract is dried on a planchette, which is placed at a fixed distance from the mica window of the G.M. tube. Sometimes the radioactivity of a slice of tissue can be determined accurately enough, merely by drying the material on to the planchette and holding it flat in front of the tube. If the tissue has appreciable thickness, a correction for self-absorption of some of the radioactivity by the specimen must be made. When the half-life of an isotope is short in relation to the length of the experiment, it is also necessary to make an allowance for natural decay of isotope during the experimental period.

Combinations of radioactive isotopes can be used to determine the absorption of both ions of a dissociated salt. This may be done by labelling one ion with a beta-emitting isotope, the other with a gamma-emitter, and measuring radioactivity before and after insertion of a tinfoil or glass screen between the sample and the mica window. From such measurements, the intensity of both gamma and beta radiation can be determined. Alternatively, combinations of short-lived and long-lived isotopes can be employed, two measurements of radioactivity being made, one before, and one after, the short-lived isotope has decayed to an appreciable extent

TABLE 6.

A LIST OF RADIOACTIVE ISOTOPES USEFUL IN THE STUDY OF SALT ABSORPTION

Isotope	Half-life	Type of radiation
^{82}Br	36 hr.	Beta, gamma
^{14}C	6000 years	Beta
^{134}Cs	2·3 years	Beta, gamma
^{137}Cs	33 years	Beta, gamma
^{45}Ca	153 days	Beta
^{36}Cl	$4·43 \times 10^5$ years	Beta
^{60}Co	5·3 years	Beta, gamma
^{131}I	8 days	Beta, gamma
^{59}Fe	45 days	Beta, gamma
^{99}Mo	68 hr.	Beta, gamma
^{32}P	14·2 days	Beta
^{42}K	12·5 hr.	Beta, gamma
^{86}Rb	19·5 days	Beta, gamma
^{22}Na	2·6 years	Beta, gamma
^{24}Na	15·0 hr.	Beta, gamma
^{35}S	87·1 days	Beta
^{85}Sr	65 days	X, gamma
^{89}Sr	51 days	Beta
^{65}Zn	245 days	Beta, gamma

(Davies and Wilkins, 1951). Apart from the convenience, accuracy and sensitivity of radioactivity determinations, the technique has the advantage that movements of ions between tissues and media can be detected and quantitatively determined, even when there is no net change of concentration (see Chapter 3 p. 32). The major disadvantages of radiochemical techniques are that expensive equipment is required, and health hazards exist which necessitate fastidious cleanliness and other precautions. For further information about the use of radioactive tracers in experiments with biological materials see, for example, Kamen (1947), Comar (1955) or Glover (1956).

73729

LIBRARY
College of St. Francis
JOLIET, ILL.

3. *Apparatus*

Various sizes and shapes of vessels are used to hold the experimental medium, depending on the plant material under investigation. Experiments may be performed on small amounts of tissue immersed in as little as 3 ml of liquid, or, on a larger scale, whole plants may be placed with their roots in 10 l. or more of solution. In any case, when solution cultures are employed, arrangements must generally be made to maintain the absorbing tissues at a constant temperature, and to supply adequate aeration. Aeration is usually achieved either by bubbling air through the solutions, or, when small volumes are involved, by mechanical shaking.

It is usual to employ a finite amount of medium and to arrange the ratio of tissue to volume of medium in such a way that a sufficiently small, but measurable, amount of salt is absorbed during the experimental period. If the medium becomes too depleted, salt concentration may become a limiting factor, and mask other factors under investigation. In prolonged experiments where it is desirable to prevent the medium from becoming much depleted a flowing solution technique may be used. Here medium is allowed to flow over the tissue or round the plant roots at a rate such that the solution emerging still contains a large part of the salt originally present. The rate of uptake of salt by the tissue can then be calculated from the decrease in concentration if the rate of flow is known. Details of such an apparatus were described by Van den Honert (1933), and by Becking (1956).

For further reading

HEWITT, E. J. (1952). Sand and water culture methods used in the study of plant nutrition. *Tech. Comm.* 22, *Commonwealth Bur. Hort. and Plantation Crops, East Malling, Kent.*

CHAPTER 3

MECHANISMS OF ION TRANSPORT

The reasoning of one who desires the possible ultimate
reference of all that takes place in the organism to
simple chemical and physical causes is as devoid of
true logic as is that of the peasant who, on seeing a
locomotive for the first time argues by analogy that a
horse must be concealed inside.

W. PFEFFER.

The Physiology of Plants (1900).

A. DEFINITIONS

Some confusion has arisen in the past among students and
investigators of salt absorption through differences in terminology.
To avoid ambiguity, a number of words will first be defined, and
then used only in that sense in the discussion which follows in
subsequent chapters. *Uptake*, *intake* and *absorption* are used
synonymously, and do not imply any particular method of entry of
salts. When these expressions are used, *net* movement is implied
unless otherwise indicated in the text. Gross uptake is sometimes
referred to as *influx* and the difference between gross and net uptake
as *efflux* (syn. *outflux*). Efflux, like influx, may occur by purely
physical processes such as diffusion and exchange, or depend upon
metabolism (*active transport*). In the former case, it is called *leakage*
and in the latter, *excretion* or *extrusion*. Active transport into
vacuoles, or into the cavities of non-living cells in the stele of roots,
is sometimes called *secretion* by analogy with similar processes in
animals.

Accumulation implies movement of ions against a concentration
gradient, generally as a result of active transport. It can also occur
passively, e.g. by the establishment of Donnan equilibria or by
adsorption. When ions are absorbed and at once incorporated
irreversibly into organic constituents of a cell, an element may be
accumulating in the organism, but the process is not referred to as
salt accumulation.

27

The term *permeability* was formerly used to describe the facility with which ions or molecules pass into, or through tissues, irrespective of the mechanism of transport (Stiles, 1924). In the text below, permeability is used synonymously with conductivity, that is, as the reciprocal of physical resistance, and thus it refers to the ease with which ions or salts can move passively through a membrane. The membrane in question may be a pauci-molecular lipoprotein layer, a layer of cytoplasm, or a layer of cells, and the structure involved should be indicated in any discussion of permeability. It is often important to distinguish between the ease with which ions penetrate into a membrane or cytoplasm (*intrability*– Höfler, 1931) and their rate of passage across it (*transmeability*– Arisz, 1945). Permeability can be expressed as grammes penetrating per hour per cm^2 of membrane surface for a given concentration gradient and temperature.

A number of physical mechanisms are involved in salt absorption, and an outline of these processes follows as a prelude to consideration of their importance in the plant.

B. DIFFUSION

If a pinch of common salt is placed in a beaker of water it dissolves, and in time becomes uniformly dispersed throughout the solution. The mechanism of dispersion, i.e. diffusion, is the random thermal movements of solute and solvent. Across any plane in a solution, particles (ions and molecules) diffuse in both directions, and it is the difference between the numbers of individual particles moving in opposite directions in a given time, or *net diffusion*, that is usually measured. Gross diffusion rates can be determined using isotopically labelled substances. When net diffusion is zero, particles continue to move in the solution at rates determined by temperature, and the nature of solute and solvent, but they move equally in all directions. Only at absolute zero ($-273\,°C$) does diffusion stop completely.

The relationship between diffusion and various factors which affect it is summarized by Fick's law:

$$dm = -D.A. \,(dc/dx)\cdot dt$$

where $dm =$ the amount of substance diffusing in time dt;

$dc/dx=$ the concentration gradient;

$A=$ area of cross-section across which diffusion occurs;

and $D=$ the diffusion coefficient.

dm is expressed in gms; dc in g/cm^3; dx in cm; t, in sec; and A in cm^2. D has the dimensions of area divided by time, and is thus expressed in cm^2 sec^{-1}.

D varies for different solutes and solvents, and is slightly affected by c, by dc/dx, and by temperature. The temperature coefficient (Q_{10}) for diffusion (i.e. the rate of diffusion at one temperature divided by that at a temperature 10 °C lower) is commonly about 1·2 for aqueous solutions. The negative sign of D is a convention indicating that diffusion occurs from a higher to a lower concentration. Fick's law applies equally to particles of solute and solvent, the only significant difference between the two, as far as diffusion is concerned, being one of relative concentration.

Salts in aqueous solution can be assigned a single diffusion coefficient, even though they are dissociated into two or more ions. This happens because the pairs or groups of oppositely charged particles do not become perceptibly separated during diffusion owing to electrical attraction; the rate of diffusion of the salt is thus determined by that of the least mobile ion species. The situation is different when an electrical potential gradient exists in the solution. Positive and negative charges then tend to move in opposite directions (electro-diffusion), in accordance with Le Chatelier's principle that movement of a charged particle tends to annul the applied potential difference. (cf. electro-osmosis, p. 32).

As in all spontaneous processes where temperature remains constant, and no energy is absorbed from the surroundings, diffusion involves dissipation of "free energy" and the "entropy" of the system increases.* Assuming that a small number of solute molecules, m, diffuse from a large volume of solution at a concentration C_1 into a similar volume at a lower concentration, C_2, both at the same temperature, the loss in free energy in the system is given by the equation:

$$-\Delta G = mRT \ln (C_1/C_2)$$

where R is the gas constant, and T, the absolute temperature.

* For a clear account of the meanings of "free energy" and "entropy," see Bull (1951).

This equation indicates the minimum amount of energy which must be supplied in transferring m molecules of solute from the lower to the higher concentration under the same conditions.

In biological systems, one is often concerned with diffusion of substances across lipid membranes which have low permeability. In these circumstances, Fick's law does not apply, even approximately. The diffusing particle has to acquire sufficient kinetic energy to overcome an appreciable potential energy barrier (μ_a) in passing from solvent into membrane, and a series of smaller potential energy barriers (μ_e) in the bulk of the membrane, before it passes into solution on the other side via the final energy barrier (μ_b) (Fig. 6a). The particle can be thought of as alternately vibrating about a mean position, and moving to a new position when it acquires sufficient energy (*activation energy*) by collisions with neighbouring particles. Such diffusion has a high Q_{10} (often 2–3) because at higher temperatures more particles acquire sufficient energy to diffuse in a given time. Diffusion may be assisted by the presence in the membrane of substances with which the penetrating particle can combine reversibly to form more soluble complexes (*facilitated diffusion*, Danielli, 1954). Facilitated diffusion resembles active transport (see below) in exhibiting saturation effects, competition between particles, and specificity, but differs in that movement is always along a concentration gradient, and metabolic energy is not directly involved.

C. MASS FLOW

A familiar example of mass flow is the discharge of liquid from a burette under the influence of gravity. Rates of mass flow can be calculated from Poiseuille's law as follows:

$$dm = -(r^4/8\eta)\cdot(dp/dx)\cdot dt$$

where dm = the quantity of liquid passing a given plane in a tube;
$\quad r$ = radius of tube;
$\quad dp/dx$ = the pressure gradient;
$\quad dt$ = time;
$\quad \eta$ = coefficient of viscosity of the liquid.

Because mass flow varies with the square of the area (r^4), whereas diffusion is proportional to area, mass flow is reduced relative to

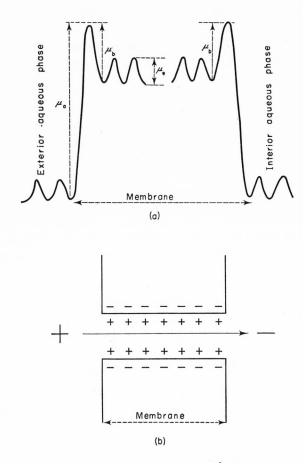

FIG. 6. Transport across membranes
a. Facilitated diffusion. Diagram illustrating the potential energy barriers in a lipid membrane (redrawn from Davson and Danielli, 1943); b. Electro-osmosis. For explanation, see text.

diffusion when the diameter of the channels through which movement occurs is reduced. This is demonstrated by the well-known fact that a dilute agar gel offers high resistance to mass flow, but allows diffusion of substances through it at a rate not very much lower than that of diffusion in water. Temperature affects the rate of mass flow by its influence on the coefficient of viscosity; theoretically mass flow is possible at absolute zero because the energy involved comes from outside the system (cf. diffusion).

In spite of its name, electro-osmosis is an example of mass flow (Fig. 6b). When one aqueous solution is separated from another by a membrane possessing charged pores, and a potential difference exists between the two solutions, mass flow of water and dissolved substances occurs. The water molecules are thought to acquire an electrical charge, opposite to that possessed by the pore walls, and then to move by electrical attraction towards the side of the membrane having the same charge as the walls. In so doing they carry along molecules of dissolved solutes.

D. Ion Exchange

If a solution of a dissociated salt (M^+A^-) is separated from distilled water by a membrane which is permeable to both ions, diffusion will occur until the concentrations of salt on the two sides are equal (Fig. 7a). Should the membrane be impermeable to either cations or anions, no diffusion of solute will occur (Fig. 7b). Now, if two solutions containing different salts ($M_1^+A_1^-$ and $M_2^+A_2^-$) are separated from one another by either a cation-permeable/anion-impermeable or cation-impermeable/anion-permeable membrane, one of the two ion species in each case is free to move across in exchange for an ion of like charge (Fig. 7c, d). Equilibrium is established when the ratio $[M_1^+]/[M_2^+]$ (in the first case) or $[A_1^-]/[A_2^-]$ (in the second case) is equal on the two sides. At equilibrium, exchange does not stop but equal relative amounts of the two cations or anions move in each direction, so that the ratio remain constant. The total concentration of salts on either side is not affected by exchange, even when a concentration gradient exists, because movement of one ion species, and therefore diffusion of salt, is prevented. Exchange involves equivalent electrical charges so that two univalent ions exchange for one bivalent, three for one trivalent ion, and so on.

When a solution of salt containing a radioactive isotope is separated by an ion exchange membrane from a non-radioactive solution of the same salt, it is possible to calculate the rates of exchange of ions between the two solutions from measurements of the changes in radioactivity with time, on either side (Ussing,

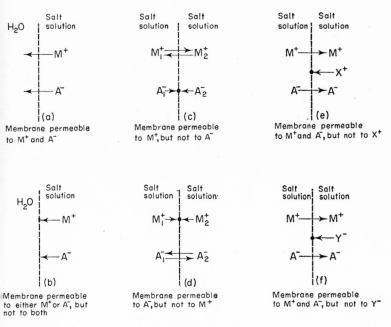

FIG. 7.   Ion exchange across membranes

1949). An equilibrium is established when the ratio of radioactive to non-radioactive ions is equal on the two sides, and the solutions are then said to have the same specific activity.

E.   Donnan Equilibria

A more complex ion-exchange system is one in which a membrane separates a solution containing ions to which the membrane is permeable, from another containing, in addition to mobile ions, either cations or anions to which it is impermeable (Fig. 7e, f.). In the simple situation represented in Fig. 7e, assuming that the concentration of the single anion ($[A^-]$) on the two sides is initially equal, the concentration of diffusable cations on the right-hand side ($[M^+]_2$) will be lower than that on the left-hand side ($[M^+]_1$) since part of the anions are balanced by X^+. Cations will thus tend to move by diffusion from left to right along a concentration gradient, but they are only able to do so if accompanied by anions which must diffuse against the concentration gradient. At equilibrium:

$$[M^+]_1 \cdot [A^-]_1 = [M^+]_2 \cdot [A^-]_2$$

where $[A^-]_1$ and $[A^-]_2$ are the concentrations of anions on the left-hand and right-hand sides respectively. At this point the electro-chemical potentials on the two sides of the membrane are equal, and the system has reached a condition of minimum free energy and maximum entropy. The total number of positive electrical charges on each side of the membrane is always balanced by an equal number of negative charges, and therefore, at equilibrium: since

$$[A^-]_1 = [M^+]_1 \text{ and } [A^-]_2 = [M^+]_2 + [X^+]_2$$

it follows that:

$$[A^-]_1 < [A^-]_2, \text{ and } [M^+]_1 > [M^+]_2$$

Similarly, in the situation represented in Fig. 7f, where immobile anions (Y^-) are present; when the system reaches equilibrium:

$$[A^-]_1 > [A^-]_2, \text{ and } [M^+]_1 < [M^+]_2$$

Since the concentrations of mobile ions (chemical potentials) are unequal on the two sides of the membrane in a Donnan system at equilibrium while the electrochemical potentials are equal, it follows that there is an electrical potential difference between the two sides.[*] This is sometimes called the Donnan membrane potential (Höber, 1947).

In the examples discussed so far, only a single pair of mobile ions was considered. If there are present in the system two or more univalent cation or anion species which can traverse the membrane, the position is a little more complicated, inasmuch as the ions distribute themselves also in accordance with the principles of ionic exchange. Thus, at equilibrium, the ratios of the concentrations of various mobile cations to one another are the same on one side as the other, and the same is true also of anions.

Bi-, tri- and multivalent ions are distributed in Donnan systems

[*] $\bar{\mu} = \mu + \psi Z F$ where $\bar{\mu}$ is the electrochemical potential; μ, the chemical potential and Z, the valency, of the ion; F, is Faraday's number, and ψ the electrical potential. For further explanation of the relationships between $\bar{\mu}$, μ and ψ, see Brönsted (1937).

according to the rules outlined, but the number of electrical charges carried by each ion must be taken into account. In general, at equilibrium:

$$\left[\frac{[M^{x+}]_1}{[M^{x+}]_2}\right]^{\frac{1}{x}} = \left[\frac{[A^{y-}]_2}{[A^{y-}]_1}\right]^{\frac{1}{y}}$$

where x and y are the valencies of the mobile cation and anion respectively. From this it follows that bi-, tri- and multivalent ions are accumulated in excess of univalent ions in Donnan systems. If for example, potassium and calcium ions are present, each at the same concentration, on the outer side on a membrane enclosing a Donnan system containing indiffusible anions, and accumulating potassium ions to a concentration of $0.01M$, calcium ions are accumulated to a concentration of $0.1M$.

The valency of immobile ions in a Donnan system does not affect the position of equilibrium, since it is the total number of electrical charges, rather than the number of particles which is relevant. For the same reason, a particular Donnan system accumulates cations or anions, but not both. In the presence of immobile anions and cations, the behaviour of the system is determined by the resultant electrical charge. The walls and protoplasts of plant cells carry an overall negative charge at pH values more alkaline than about 4 and therefore behave as Donnan systems containing indiffusible anions. For a further discussion of Donnan equilibria and their establishment in biological systems, see Vervelde (1953).

F. ADSORPTION

Solutes tend to accumulate at interfaces if surface tension is thereby lowered, and this process is called "adsorption". Both cations and anions are adsorbed from aqueous solutions on to the surface of many cell constituents, including cellulose and proteins.

The relationship between amount of solute adsorbed and concentration in the aqueous phase is indicated approximately by the equation:

$$a = mKCn$$

where m = the amount of adsorbent

$\quad\quad C$ = external concentration

$\quad\quad K$ and n are constants for particular solutes and adsorbents.

When a/m is plotted against C, the familiar Freundlich adsorption isotherm is obtained (Fig. 8a), and if log a/m is plotted against log C a straight line results with slope $=$ n, and intercept on the ordinate $=$ log K, in accordance with the equation:

$$\log a/m = \log K + n \log C$$

The Freundlich relationship is an empirical one which holds fairly well at low values of C, but breaks down at high concentrations where the adsorbent approaches saturation.

Another way of expressing the relationship between adsorption and concentration is by the Langmuir equation which has general application in physical chemistry. In this case:

$$a/m = (k_1 C)/(1 + k_2 C) \text{ where } k_1, k_2 \text{ are constants.}$$

At high values of C, unity can be neglected and the equation reduces to:

$$a/m = k_1/k_2$$

k_1/k_2 is thus the saturation value for a given adsorbent. If experimental data fit the Langmuir equation, a straight line is obtained when the reciprocal of a/m is plotted against the reciprocal of C. Fig. 8b shows that adsorption of acetic acid on charcoal occurs according to the Langmuir equation.

It is sometimes convenient to distinguish between two kinds of adsorption—mechanical and polar. Both depend on the operation of electrical forces at the adsorbing surface, but they differ in the strength of binding. Mechanical adsorption involves weak residual and secondary valencies, and substances adsorbed in this way are removable by washing in water. Polar adsorption on the other hand depends on the formation of salts, e.g. between an alkali cation (K^+) and a carboxyl group of an organic molecule, as follows:

$$K^+ + R.COO^- \rightleftharpoons R.COOK$$

or between an anion (e.g. Cl^-) and a basic group, e.g.

$$Cl^- + R.NH_3^+ \rightleftharpoons R.NH_3Cl$$

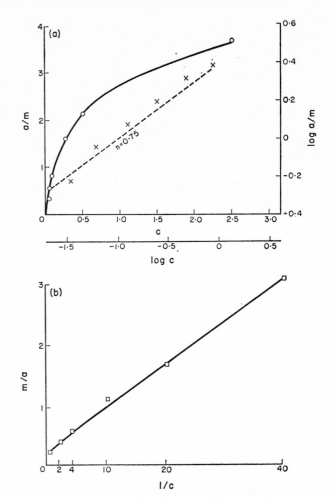

FIG. 8. Absorption of acetic acid on charcoal
a. Conventional plot (○—○) and log/log plot (x---x) of the same data.
b. Double reciprocal plot of the data presented in a.

Polar adsorption frequently involves simultaneous displacement of another ion (*adsorption exchange*), e.g.

$$K^+ + R.COOH \rightleftharpoons R.COOK + H^+$$

Ion exchange resins function in this way. A sulphonated polystyrene resin in the acid form, R.SO$_3$H) for example, reacts with sodium chloride to produce the sodium salt of the resin and hydrochloric acid:

$$R.SO_3H + NaCl \rightleftharpoons R.SO_3Na + HCl$$

In presence of excess acid, the reaction is reversed and the acid form of the resin is regenerated.

Anion exchange resins similarly react reversibly with salts, adsorbing anions from neutral solutions and releasing them in presence of dilute alkalis, e.g.:

$$R.OH + NaCl \rightleftharpoons R.Cl + NaOH$$

Both mechanical and polar adsorption are involved in the staining

(a)   (b)

Fig. 9.   Adsorption of dyes by amphoteric molecules
a. Amphoteric adsorbent on the acid side of its isoelectric point, and positively charged. Coloured acid dye adsorbed; b. Amphoteric adsorbent cation of basic dye adsorbed.

by dyes of biological materials such as cellulose and proteins. Basic dyes e.g. methylene blue (MeCl$_2$) in which the coloured part of the molecule is positively charged, are adsorbed by substances containing a predominance of negative charges. Acidic dyes, e.g. orange G (HG) on the other hand, contain coloured anions, and stain positively charged materials. The capacity of amphoteric substances, e.g. proteins to take up dyes, depends on the charge carried by the adsorbent, and hence on the pH value of the surrounding medium (Fig. 9).

G.   Chemical Combination

There is no very clear distinction between polar adsorption and chemical combination, but the latter tends to have a higher Q_{10}

and to be less easily reversed. When the dye crystal violet is adsorbed by charcoal, the coloured anion is adsorbed and the solution becomes more acid. In these circumstances, the dye can be readily washed out again with dilute acid. If, however, the solution is brought to neutrality, the dye forms a condensation product which involves chemical combination and is then not easily removed.

Chelation is a well-known mechanism of chemical combination between certain organic substances and bi- or trivalent cations in which the ions are held partly by co-ordinate bonds in undissociated complexes. One of the best-known synthetic chelating agents is ethylene diaminetetra-acetic acid (Fig. 10), and amongst the

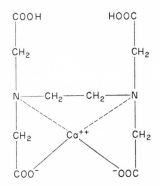

FIG. 10. Ethylene diaminetetra-acetic acid

naturally occurring chelators are citric acid, pyridoxal, nucleic acids and proteins.

Actively metabolizing cells are unique in their capacity to incorporate ions, especially anions, into organic cell constituents through enzyme reactions. Nitrate, sulphate and phosphate are converted into permanent structural components, and such incorporation continues as long as the cell grows. In addition, both cations and anions are held temporarily in more labile complexes, e.g. with enzymes and metabolic intermediates. This process is referred to as "labile chemical binding".

Chemical combination may instigate salt absorption by creating and maintaining a concentration gradient along which ions can diffuse. This mechanism resembles facilitated diffusion in that a high degree of specificity may be exhibited through the chemical reactions which control binding, but it differs in being directly dependent on metabolic energy (cf. active transport).

H.   ACTIVE TRANSPORT

When ions are moved across a membrane by a mechanism which is directly dependent on metabolic energy, they are said to be transported "actively". Most of the hypotheses advanced to explain

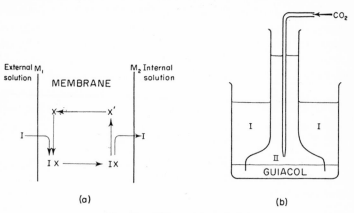

FIG. 11.   The carrier concept
a. General concept of a carrier mechanism. For explanation, see text;
b. Diagrammatic representation of a model carrier mechanism (Osterhout and Stanley, 1932). For explanation, see text.

active transport involve reversible binding of ions to a constituent of the membrane which acts as a "carrier". Although it is very likely that something of this kind happens, the operation of carrier systems has not yet been demonstrated unequivocally.

According to the "carrier" concept (Fig. 11), an ion reacts with its carrier (X) at, or near, the outer surface (M_1) of the membrane. This reaction might involve adsorption, exchange adsorption, or some kind of chemical combination. Neither the carrier nor the ion-carrier complex (IX) can move into the medium, but IX is mobile in the membrane, and moves to the other side (M_2). Here it breaks down, releasing the ion into the internal solution and forming a carrier precursor (X^1) which is incapable of leaving the membrane, or of reaccepting an ion. X^1 is transported back across the membrane and reconverted to X, where at M_1 it can combine with another ion. Thus a limited number of carrier molecules are capable of transporting an indefinite amount of salt. Efficient active transport requires the presence of a rather impermeable membrane, since otherwise ions transported by a carrier mechanism against a concentration gradient diffuse in the opposite direction and accumulation is prevented or reduced.

The functioning of a carrier mechanism for ions can be demonstrated with a simple chemical model (Fig. 11b). An aqueous solution (I) containing potassium chloride and potassium hydroxide is separated from water (II) by a layer of guiacol. If carbon dioxide is bubbled through II, potassium ions migrate across the guiacol and eventually may attain a higher concentration in II than in I. The explanation is as follows: potassium hydroxide reacts with guiacol (HG) where the latter is in contact with I, according to the equation:

$$KOH + HG \rightarrow KG + H_2O$$

Potassium guiacolate (KG) forms, diffuses through the layer of guiacol along a concentration gradient, and is decomposed at the surface in contact with II, as follows:

$$KG + H_2CO_3 \rightarrow KHCO_3 + HG$$

Guiacol is thus reformed, while potassium ions accumulate in II as potassium bicarbonate. In this model, guiacol molecules act as carriers, and transport continues as long as potassium ions remain in solution I and the pH gradient is maintained.

A similar model can be designed to accumulate anions, e.g. chloride across a layer of a suitable organic base (YOH) as a result of the reactions:

$$HCl + YOH \rightarrow YCl + H_2O \text{ on one side}$$
$$\text{and } YCl + KOH \rightarrow YOH + KCl \text{ on the other.}$$

In this case transport occurs from a more acid to a more alkaline solution. It is not possible to combine the two mechanisms in a model which will accumulate both ions of a neutral salt in the same solution because cations and anions move in opposite directions in the presence of a pH gradient (cf. p. 74).

In order to understand any carrier mechanism which may be operative in plants, it is necessary to know:

(i) the mechanism of movement of the ion-carrier complex;

(ii) the nature of the substances involved, and

(iii) the reactions they undergo.

One suggestion regarding (i) is that carrier and ion may form a lipid soluble complex which can diffuse across a lipoprotein membrane along a concentration gradient (Fig. 12a). Another possibility is that the carrier or part of it is capable of rotating in some way in the membrane, and thus of transferring ions bound at one surface across to the other (Fig. 12b i, ii). Some device would be necessary to ensure that the binding site returns to the outer surface unloaded to receive another ion. Alternatively, the carrier might be a strongly surface-active substance which slides along the walls of water-filled pores in the membrane with the polar head to which ions are bound in the water phase, and the lipophilic tail associated with lipid materials in the membrane (Fig. 12c). Phosphatides appear to be particularly well suited for such a purpose, and they are known to be constituents of biological membranes.

As an alternative to the passive propulsion of ion-carrier complexes by physical processes, mechanisms more directly dependent on metabolism have been suggested. If, for example, the carrier forms part of a contractile molecule of protein, transport may be accomplished by rhythmic contraction and expansion of the polypeptide chain (Fig. 12d). Again, contractile proteins in a membrane might procure transport of bound ions from one side to another by causing vesiculation (pinocytosis). When the process is completed, the droplet within the membrane may disintegrate to release the bound ions (Fig. 12e).

In the active transport of salts, the movement of one ion cannot be considered without reference to that of another of opposite sign. One possibility is that each is absorbed independently by an exchange process involving metabolically-produced cations and anions (Fig. 13 a, b). Linked absorption of two ionic species need not necessarily involve the active transport of both. If, for example, cations are actively transported across a membrane which is impermeable only to cations, uptake of anions might occur passively along the electrical gradient created by accumulation of the positively charged ions

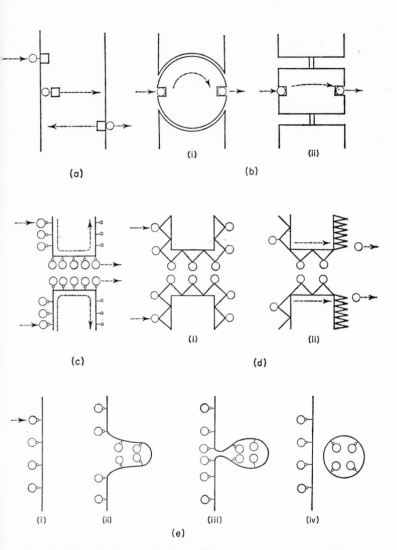

Fig. 12. Hypothetical mechanisms of ion transport across membranes. Ions are indicated O.
a. Diffusing carriers; b. Rotating carriers; c. Sliding carriers; d. Propelled carriers (as suggested by Goldacre and Lorch, 1950); e. Membrane vesicula- (as suggested by Bennett, 1956).

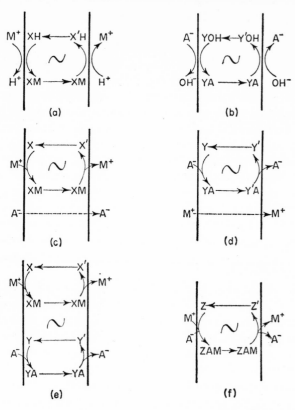

FIG. 13.   Interrelationships between cation and anion transport
a. Active cation transport involving exchange; b. active anion transport
involving exchange; c. Active cation transport accompanied by passive
anion absorption; d. Active anion transport accompanied by passive cation
transport; e. Active transport of cations and anions by separate carrier
systems; f. Active transport of cations and anions by a common carrier
system.

(Fig. 13c). Alternatively, active transport of anions might create
the necessary electrochemical gradient for passive cation accumulation across a cation-permeable barrier (Fig. 13d).

Active transport could equally be involved in the movement of
both cations and anions across an impermeable membrane. The
system might comprise separate carriers linked through a common
energy supply (Fig. 13e) or there might be an amphoteric carrier

molecule, capable of transporting both cations and anions simultaneously (Fig. 13f). Measurements of the passive permeability of membranes and the potential differences existing across them may help to distinguish between the possibilities listed, but there is not yet general agreement about the situation in plants. In yeast, and bacteria, cation movements seem to involve exchange and to be largely unrelated to transport of anions (mechanism a), while in roots, mechanism d has received strong support from Lundegårdh (1954).

Even though the whole concept of carrier systems is still in doubt, there has been no lack of speculation about the nature of carrier molecules. Enzymes ("permeases" or "translocases"), structural proteins, peptides, amino acids, ribonucleic acid, phosphatides (e.g. lecithin), pyridoxal, cytochromes and sugar phosphates have been suggested as possible carriers. The manner in which some of them might function in the transport of salts is discussed below (Chapters 5 and 6).

The relationship between external concentration and active transport involving a carrier, resembles that between concentration and adsorption, and can similarly be represented by the Freundlich and Langmuir equations. Active transport may be treated kinetically using a modification of the Langmuir equation which was applied by Lineweaver and Burk (1934) to enzyme kinetics. If an ion combines with a carrier to produce an intermediate complex which subsequently breaks down, the reactions can be represented thus:

$$I+X \underset{k_2}{\overset{k_1}{\rightleftharpoons}} XI \underset{k_4}{\overset{k_3}{\rightleftharpoons}} X^1+I$$

where I, X, X^1 and XI are the ion, ion carrier, carrier precursor, and ion-carrier complex respectively (cf. Fig. 11a), and $k_{1\text{-}4}$) are the rate constants of the reactions, as indicated. In such a sequence, the rate of transport (v) is related to the concentration of the ion $[I]$ as follows:

$$v=(V[I])/(K_s+[I])$$

where V is the maximum rate of transport when the carrier system is fully saturated. K_s is a constant, corresponding to the Michaelis constant in enzyme kinetics, $(=(k_2 \times k_3)k_1$ when k_4 is negligible), and it is equal to the concentration of salt at which v reaches 50 per cent of its maximum value. On plotting $1/v$ against $1/s$ a straight line is obtained for which the ordinate intercept is $1/V$ and the slope $= K_s/V$ (cf. Fig. 8b). The application of this treatment to salt absorption data is discussed in more detail below (p. 58). It must be emphasized that kinetic studies do not assist in distinguishing between the various general mechanisms represented in Figs. 12 and 13, or in elucidating the chemical nature of the hypothetical carriers. They do, however, supply evidence which is consistent with the operation of a carrier system.

For further reading

BROYER, T. C. (1947). The movement of materials into plants. II. The nature of solute movement into plants. *Bot. Rev.* **13**, 125–67.

OVERSTREET, R. and JACOBSON, L. (1952). Mechanisms of ion absorption by roots. *Ann. Rev. Plant Physiol.* **3**, 189–206.

ROBERTSON, R. N. (1958). The uptake of minerals. *Encycl. Plant Physiol.* IV. 243–79.

ROSENBERG, T. (1954). The concept and definition of active transport. *Symp. Soc. Exp. Biol.* **8**, 27–41.

CHAPTER 4

FACTORS AFFECTING SALT ABSORPTION

Science is based solely on properties and facts ascertained by experiment and observation, that is to say on a knowledge that under given conditions certain results must necessarily be obtained.

W. PFEFFER.
The Physiology of Plants (1900).

A. EXTERNAL FACTORS

1. *Temperature*

The rate of salt absorption tends to increase with increasing temperatures until a maximum rate is reached, and then to decrease again at still higher temperatures (Fig. 14a). At temperatures above about 40 °C, absorption is progressively reduced in many plants, presumably because of the gradual inactivation of enzyme systems involved. In addition, the cytoplasm becomes more permeable to passive leakage of salts through it at high temperatures, so that if a concentration gradient exists, net absorption is reduced as the temperature is raised. At temperatures approaching 0 °C, absorption decreases both by diminution in the rate of chemical reactions involved in active transport, and by increased viscosity, and hence higher resistance, of the cell membranes.

Total salt absorption either by a cell or whole plant can be separated into two components, one with a Q_{10} of about 1·2 and another with a Q_{10} of 2–3 or higher. The salt taken up in a short time by a tissue at 1–2 °C is thought to be absorbed mainly by physical processes (diffusion, mass flow, exchange and adsorption), while that absorbed at higher temperatures includes also a component dependent on respiration. Physical absorption is completed relatively rapidly, whereas the period of metabolic absorption is prolonged (Fig. 14b).

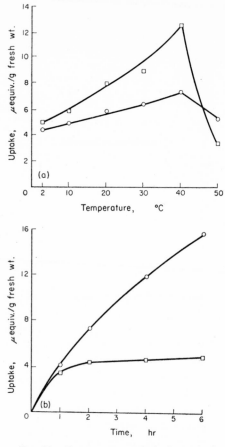

FIG. 14.   Temperature and salt absorption

a. Absorption of potassium ions by washed carrot tissue slices at different temperatures in 30 min (○) and 2 hr (□) Sutcliffe (unpublished); b. The time course of potassium absorption by washed carrot tissue slices at 2 °C (□) and 20 °C (○) Sutcliffe (unpublished).

2. *Light*

The effects of light on salt absorption are mainly indirect. Visible light supplies energy for uptake in green plants through photosynthesis, and, in addition, the gaseous exchange associated with this process creates conditions favourable to active metabolism and ion accumulation (see below).   Light also has effects on the

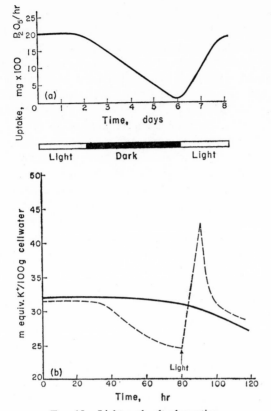

FIG. 15. Light and salt absorption

a. Absorption of phosphate by maize plants during successive periods of light and darkness (redrawn from Alberda, 1948); b. Influence of light and darkness on the potassium content of *Ulva lactuca*.——plants in continuous light; — — — plants transferred from darkness to light after 80 hr (redrawn from Scott and Hayward, 1953).

structure of leaves and the condition of stomata, which influence transpiration, and thus indirectly affects salt absorption (see p. 112f).

It is known that photosynthetic organisms kept in the dark gradually cease to absorb salts and finally release them as respiratory substrates become depleted. Alberda (1948) found that the rate of absorption of phosphate by maize plants fell to zero about 4 days after they were transferred from light to darkness, and began to rise again as soon as they were reilluminated (Fig. 15a). Ketchum

(1939) observed that *Nitzschia closterium* (a marine diatom) will normally absorb phosphate only in the light, but it can be induced to do so to a limited extent in the dark if the cells have previously been grown in light under conditions of phosphate deficiency. Dark-induced absorption may depend on chemical combination between the ions and binding substances which are synthesized in the light. *Ulva* cells gradually lose potassium ions when kept in the dark and reabsorb them upon reillumination (Fig. 15b). The reason for the temporary increase in potassium content to a supra-optimal level soon after transfer of the plants from darkness to light, followed by a rapid decrease to the normal level, is not clear.

An interesting light-dependent ion transport mechanism was observed in the leaves of certain water plants by Arens (1936) and has been further studied by Steemann Nielsen (1951) and Lowen-haupt (1956). Briefly, when a solution of calcium bicarbonate is applied to the abaxial surface of a *Potomogeton* leaf in the light, salt is absorbed and calcium ions are subsequently excreted, together with hydroxyl ions, on the other side. The cation movement ceases in the dark or when salts other than bicarbonate are supplied, and is presumably linked to utilization of bicarbonate in photosynthesis.

Ultra-violet light inhibits salt absorption and may cause leakage of ions from cells. Destruction of lipo-protein complexes which participate in the maintenance of the semi-permeability of protoplasm, and decomposition of ribonucleic acid, have been implicated in this effect (Lepeschkin, 1930; Tanada, 1955).

3. *Oxygen Pressure*

In the absence of oxygen, the metabolic component of salt absorption is inhibited in aerobic organisms. Vlamis and Davis (1944) found that excised roots of various plants showed maximum absorption at oxygen concentrations of 2–3 per cent, and higher concentrations up to 100 per cent did not increase the rate of uptake further (Fig. 16a). Hopkins (1956) found that phosphate absorption by excised barley roots is independent of the partial pressure of oxygen over the range 3–100 per cent when the total gas pressure is kept at 1 atm. Over the range 3–0 per cent a hyperbolic relationship was observed with 0·3 per cent giving half of the maximum rate (Fig. 16b).

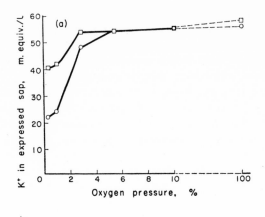

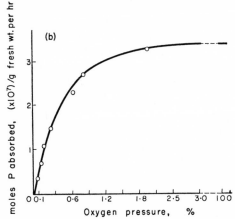

FIG. 16.   Oxygen pressure and salt absorption

a. Relationship between oxygen pressure and the potassium content of excised tomato roots (○—○) and excised rice roots (▫—▫) (redrawn from Vlamis and Davis, 1944); b. Relationship between oxygen pressure and phosphate absorption by excised barley roots in solutions of phosphate $(1 \times 10^{-4} M)$ at pH 4 (redrawn from Hopkins, 1956).

4. *Carbon dioxide and Bicarbonate Ion Concentration*

The dependence of salt absorption in green plants on photosynthesis has already been mentioned. In the absence of carbon dioxide, uptake of salt is gradually inhibited, as respiratory substrates become depleted.

Dark fixation of carbon dioxide in non-green tissues has an

interesting effect on the differential absorption of anions and cations. When carbon dioxide is fixed, organic acids are synthesized in the cells and hydrogen ions apparently exchange for other cations from the external medium causing salts of organic acids to accumulate. In this way, absorption of cations in excess of anions, may occur. (Jacobson and Ordin, 1954). In some tissues placed in alkaline media, the apparent excess absorption of cations over anions is balanced by uptake of bicarbonate ions, which are converted to organic acid anions within the tissue (Hurd and Sutcliffe, 1957; Hurd 1958: see Fig. 17 a, b and also Fig. 33 p. 92).

Carbon dioxide and bicarbonate ions at high concentrations aveh inhibitory effects on salt absorption as on other physiological processes. Steward and Preston (1941) found that at various pH values of the medium, the effect of a simultaneous increase of carbon dioxide and bicarbonate concentrations was to inhibit bromide absorption by potato slices. Chang and Loomis (1945) similarly observed that absorption of salt by wheat (*Triticum aestivum*), maize and rice plants, was reduced to a greater extent by bubbling carbon dioxide through the nutrient solution for 10 minutes out of every hour than it was by similar treatment with nitrogen. These observations may receive a partial explanation in the fact that cytochrome oxidase activity in mitochondrial preparations and whole roots is inhibited by bicarbonate ions at high concentrations (Miller and Evans, 1956).

5. *Hydrogen Ion Concentration*

The pH value of the medium affects salt absorption in several ways. Bicarbonate ions, for example, accumulate in alkaline solutions and this may lead to enhanced cation absorption by increasing the effective concentration of salt (Fig. 17 a, b). If, however, bicarbonate or hydroxyl ions compete with other anions, for example chloride, or nitrate, absorption of these may be reduced at high pH values. In agreement with this contention, Hoagland and Davis (1923) found that *Nitella* cells absorb nitrate and chloride more rapidly from an acid than from an alkaline medium. Olsen (1953) showed that inhibition of anion absorption at alkaline pH values in *Elodea canadensis* was greater at low than at high salt concentrations, presumably because bicarbonate ions compete more effectively when the ratio of bicarbonate to other anions is high.

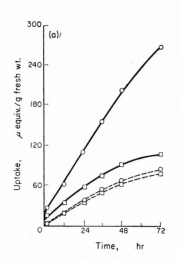

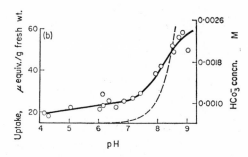

FIG. 17 (a-b).   pH and salt absorption

a. Absorption of K$^+$(—) and Cl$^-$ (---) by washed red beet root slices at 25 °C from 0·0024 M. potassium chloride solutions buffered at pH 6 (□) and pH 8·5 (○) (redrawn from Hurd and Sutcliffe, 1957); b. Absorption of K$^+$ by washed red beet root slices in 6 hr at 25 °C from 0·0024 M. potassium chloride solutions at different pH values (○—○); and the theoretical) amounts of HCO$_3$ retained in solution under the same conditions (---) (redrawn from Hurd and Sutcliffe, 1957)

In solutions which were freed of bicarbonate ions the amount of nitrate absorbed was found to be independent of pH values between 4 and 9. Van den Honert and Hooymans (1955) demonstrated that uptake of nitrate by maize plants decreases with increasing pH value (Fig. 17c), and concluded that hydrogen ion concentration rather

5

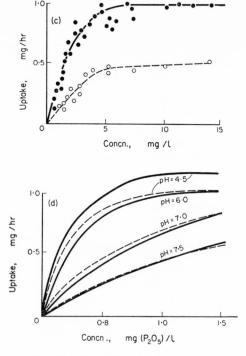

FIG. 17 (c-d).   pH and salt absorption.
c. Relationship between nitrate concentrations and the rate of absorption by maize plants at pH 6·0 (—) and pH 7·4 (---) (redrawn from Van den Honert and Hooymans, 1955). d. Relationship between phosphate concentration and rate of absorption by maize plants at various pH values of the medium. Solid lines represent experimental data; dashed lines calculated on the assumptions that only univalent ions are absorbed, and that pH affects absorption only by altering the ratio of various phosphate ions in solution (redrawn from Van den Honert, 1933).

than competition with bicarbonate ions was responsible, because varying the concentration of bicarbonate when the pH value was kept constant did not affect nitrate absorption.

The concentration of hydrogen ions in the medium has an especially important effect on phosphate absorption because over the physiological range of pH values the predominant ionic form shifts from univalent ($H_2PO_4^-$), to bivalent ($HPO_4^=$) and finally to trivalent ($PO_4^\equiv$) as the medium becomes more alkaline. Van den

Honert (1933) studied the effect of pH on phosphate absorption by sugar cane plants and found the results to be consistent with the view that only univalent ions are absorbed to an appreciable extent (Fig. 17d). Hagen and Hopkins (1955) concluded that the effects of Hp on uptake of phosphate by excised barley roots can be explained in terms of the differential rates of absorption and relative concentrations of uni- and bivalent ions in solution. Arnon *et al.* (1942) decided that the deleterious effects of alkaline pH values on growth of some plants may be attributed to their inability to absorb sufficient phosphate under these conditions.

Increase in the hydrogen ion concentration of the medium generally causes a decrease in the rate of absorption of cations, probably as a result of competition between the similarly charged ions for binding and carrier sites (cf. p. 58). Osterhout (1936) believed that cation accumulation is only possible when the pH of the medium is more alkaline than that of the cell sap (see p. 76). Hoagland and Broyer (1942) reported, however, that excised barley roots will absorb potassium and other cations when the external medium is more acid than the apparent pH value of the cell sap, although they do so at a reduced rate. At extremely acid pH values, net uptake of salt may be depressed by damage to the cell membranes which results in increased passive leakage of salts from vacuoles.

6. *External Concentration*

The early work of Stiles and Kidd (1919) indicated that the relationship between external concentration and absorption in tissue slices resembles the Freundlich adsorption isotherm. More recent investigators (Helder, 1952; Epstein and Hagen, 1952) have put greater emphasis on the validity of the Langmuir equation (cf. Chapter 3, p. 36). Data on the effect of external concentration on the absorption of rubidium by excised barley roots show that both relationships are applicable as a first approximation (Fig. 18a).

Uptake and external concentration are often, but not always, related to one another in the manner just described. Departures from the hyperbolic relationship may be expected if:

(*a*) the adsorption sites or carrier molecules are saturated with salt, so that uptake depends on the rate of synthesis of unoccupied binding sites,

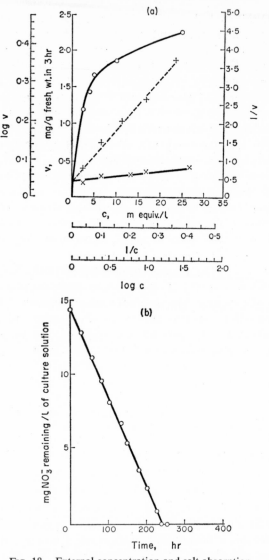

FIG. 18.   External concentration and salt absorption
a. Relation between external concentration and absorption of Rb⁺ by barley
roots plotted conventionally (O—O) as reciprocals (×——×) and as logar-
ithms (+ – – – +) (data from Epstein and Hagen, 1952); b. The nitrate concentration of the nutrient medium at different times during the absorption of
salt by rye plants (redrawn from Olsen, 1950).

(b) diffusion is a limiting factor in transport of ions to the binding sites, or

(c) a fraction of the salt absorbed is taken up passively by mass flow.

Where diffusion or mass flow are involved, absorption tends to become directly proportional to concentration, and, when the carrier system is saturated, independent of it. Kostytschew (1926) maintained that plants absorb about the same amounts of salt from dilute as from more concentrated solutions, and Olsen (1950) demonstrated that the rate of uptake of nitrate and phosphate by rye plants is unaffected by external concentration over a wide range (Fig. 18b). Olsen concluded that the rate at which individual ions are absorbed is determined by the ratio of their concentration to those of other ions in the medium, rather than by concentration itself.

Knaus and Porter (1954) noticed that the relationship between concentration and absorption of salt by *Chlorella* cells varies for different ions. For several cations, uptake is directly proportional to concentration, whereas absorption of sulphate and phosphate varies directly as the logarithm of external concentration when the medium is dilute, and becomes independent of concentration in stronger solutions. Steward and Millar (1954) reported an interesting difference between rapidly growing and slowly growing carrot cells in tissue culture. In the former, caesium absorption was found to increase linearly, and in the latter logarithmically, with increasing concentration.

7. *Interaction between Ions*

Ions in a solution affect the absorption of one another in a variety of ways, and the more ion species there are present, the more complex the situation becomes. From single salt solutions, cations tend to be absorbed more rapidly in the presence of a readily absorbable anion than of one which is taken up more slowly, and vice versa. The radius of the hydrated ion is one of the factors influencing the rate at which individual ionic species are absorbed, and in general, for this reason univalent ions are absorbed more rapidly than are bivalent and multivalent ions. Inherent preferences exhibited by the absorption system are, however, of paramount importance, and potassium, for example, is usually absorbed more rapidly than other alkali cations, although both rubidium and caesium have smaller hydrated ions. Similarly, chloride is absorbed more rapidly than the smaller bromide and iodide ions.

When two or more ion species with the same electrical sign are present in the external medium, either antagonistic or synergistic effects may be observed. It had often been found that chemically related anions interfere with one another during absorption whereas more diverse anions do not. Chloride uptake is, for example, reduced in the presence of bromide or iodide, but may be unaffected or even stimulated when nitrate or phosphate is present; sulphate and selenate have been shown to compete with one another for uptake in a variety of plants, as also do arsenate and phosphate.

Effects of such anions as nitrate, phosphate and sulphate in stimulating the absorption of other ions is probably due to enhancement of metabolism. Helder (1952) demonstrated that nitrate uptake by maize plants ceases in the absence of phosphate, and he attributed this to cessation of synthetic processes, involving phosphate, in which nitrate is utilized. Similarly, absorption of potassium and other cations by whole plants growing in solution culture soon stops when nitrate or other metabolically important anions are withheld from the medium.

The alkali cations compete with one another to a greater or lesser extent for absorption and the uptake of one is generally reduced when the concentration of another is increased. With certain reservations arising from the fact that absorption of cations is interrelated to that of associated anions, such competition can be treated kinetically in the same way as inhibition of enzyme reactions (Fig. 19). If two ions compete with one another, the straight lines obtained when the reciprocal of the initial rate of absorption of one ion $(1/v)$ is plotted against the reciprocal of concentration $(1/[I]$, at different concentrations of a competitor, cut the ordinate at the same point corresponding to $1/V$ (Fig. 19 ab cf. 45-6). When noncompetitive inhibition occurs, the reciprocal plots tend to give straight lines parallel to one another (Fig. 19d). The results of Fig. 19 indicate that potassium, rubidium and caesium compete with one another for the same carrier sites in barley roots. In the case of sodium and lithium, the data cannot be interpreted unequivocally because the addition of a competing cation raises the total salt concentration and may therefore enhance rubidium absorption, thus offsetting some or all of the depressive effect of the competing cation. (Sutcliffe, 1959).

Alkali cations do not compete with one another on equal terms and potassium absorption, for example, is not usually as strongly

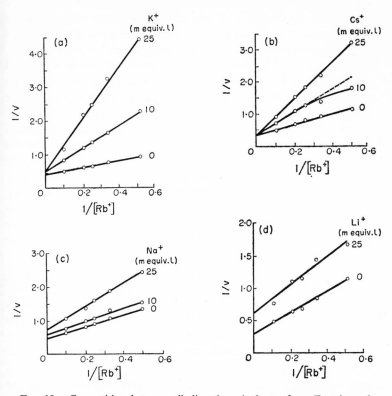

FIG. 19. Competition between alkali cations (redrawn from Epstein and Hagen, 1952).   (For explanation, see text).

inhibited by the presence of sodium, as sodium uptake is reduced by potassium. This is shown very clearly in the case of seaweeds, which absorb potassium more rapidly than sodium, in spite of the much larger amount of sodium in sea-water (see Fig. 2, p. 11). G. T. Scott (1943) showed that the sodium content of *Chlorella* cells increases when they are grown in potassium-deficient media, indicating that sodium absorption is normally restricted by the presence of potassium. Many similar observations have been made upon higher plants growing in soil.

The physical component of absorption exhibits little discrimination between the alkali cations, selectivity being confined mainly to the metabolic component. In principle, selective absorption can be explained in terms of either separate binding or carrier sites for various ions, differing in number and turnover rate, or a common absorption mechanism which binds and transports certain ions in preference to others. In the first case, the active uptake of a particular ion species should be unaffected by the presence of another, but in the second, uptake of one ion is reduced when a competing ion is present. Both these situations can apparently arise, and it seems probable that potassium and sodium compete in cells for a number of binding sites which have varying degrees of preference. (Epstein and Hagen, 1952; Fried and Noggle, 1958; Bange, 1959). In yeast (Conway, 1955), and in some seaweeds, including *Ulva lactuca*, a mechanism with a high potassium preference transports ions inwards, whereas a sodium-preferring mechanism causes excretion of this ion from the cells (see p. 154-5).

A number of observations have been made on the absorption of the alkali earth cations by plant cells. Magnesium is apparently taken up actively at sites which are distinct from those involved in the uptake of calcium, barium and strontium (Collander, 1941; G. T. Scott, 1943; Epstein and Leggett, 1954).

When alkali cations and alkali earth cations are mixed in the external medium, uptake of the latter is commonly depressed whilst that of the former is often enhanced. Viets (1944) showed that a number of bivalent ions, including calcium, stimulate potassium and bromide absorption by excised barley roots at some concentrations, and are inhibitory at others (Fig. 20a). Overstreet *et al.* (1952) confirmed these effects of calcium on uptake of potassium and attributed them to a dual influence on the absorption mechanism. They suggested that calcium competes with potassium for its absorption sites, and this results in inhibition of potassium uptake when the ratio of calcium to potassium is high (Fig. 20c). In addition calcium has a stimulatory effect on active transport, possibly by facilitating the breakdown of the potassium-carrier complex. Calcium absorption by barley roots falls rapidly at first as the potassium concentration of the medium is raised, and then decreases

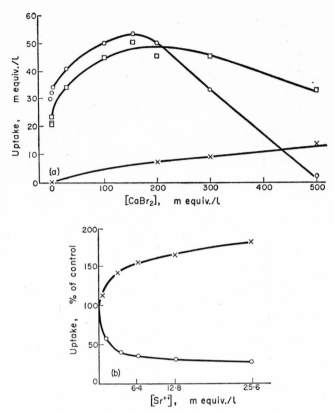

FIG. 20 (a-b). Interactions between univalent and bivalent ions
a. Effects of calcium bromide concentrations on absorption by excised barley roots of K^+ ($\odot$—$\odot$) Ca^{++} (x—x) and Br^- ($\square$—$\square$) from solutions of 0·005 M. potassium bromide, containing varying amounts of calcium bromide (redrawn from Viets, 1944); b. Effects of strontium concentration on absorption of rubidium by carrot disks in 5 min ($\odot$—$\odot$) and 24 hr (x—x) (redrawn from Middleton and Russell, 1958).

more slowly (Fig. 20d). This is explained by supposing that calcium is taken up by two separate mechanisms one of which is strongly inhibited by potassium and the other less so.

The effect of strontium ions on absorption of rubidium by carrot disks was examined by Middleton and Russell (1958). They found that in a short experimental period, rubidium uptake was depressed by increasing strontium concentration, presumably

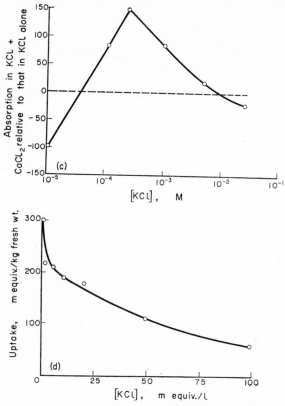

FIG. 20 (c-d).   Interactions between univalent and bivalent ions.
c. Effect of adding calcium chloride (0·01 N) on absorption of potassium
ions from different concentrations of potassium chloride by excised barley
roots (redrawn from Overstreet, Jacobson and Handley, 1952); d. Effects of
adding potassium chloride at various concentrations on absorption of calcium
from 0·005 N. calcium chloride by excised barley roots (redrawn from
Overstreet, Jacobson and Handley, 1952).

through competition for physical binding sites. Over a longer
period, however, rubidium absorption was enhanced by the presence
of strontium through an effect upon metabolic absorption (Fig. 20b).
Synergistic effects are not confined to those between univalent and
bivalent cations. Fawzy *et al.* (1954) found that trivalent ions, e.g.
aluminium, cerium and lanthanum, stimulate uptake of univalent
cations in excised barley roots.

8. *Influence of other Constituents of the Medium*

a. Osmotic effects. There are some reports that salt absorption occurs less rapidly in highly turgid than in flaccid cells and tissues. Jacques (1938), for example, observed that the rate of absorption of potassium ions by mature *Valonia* coenocytes is increased when the pressure exerted by the protoplasm on the inelastic cellulose wall is artificially relieved. The same effect occurs in red beet tissue, when the osmotic pressure of the medium is increased (Sutcliffe 1954a). When beet cells are plasmolysed, however, potassium absorption is depressed to a lower level than that observed in turgid cells. This does not seem to be due to decreased surface area of the protoplast, increased thickness, or increased concentration of solutes in the vacuole, because inhibition does not apparently increase with increasing extent of plasmolysis. Absorption of salt by plasmolysed cells can occur when the internal concentration of the sap is higher than would be necessary to prevent absorption in turgid tissue (see pp. 65-66).

In intact tomato plants Long (1943) showed that water uptake can be reduced to as much as 20 per cent of its original value by addition of sodium chloride or sucrose to the medium without an effect on nitrate absorption. Brouwer (1954) similarly found that increasing the osmotic pressure of the medium caused a considerable reduction in water uptake without much affecting absorption of chloride by intact *Vicia faba* plants (cf. Chapter 7, p. 116). Arisz and Schreuder (1956) observed no effect of external osmotic pressure on the uptake of salt by *Vallisneria* leaves unless plasmolysis occurred, when there was a considerable decrease in uptake.

b. Effects through metabolism. There are a number of substances which either stimulate or inhibit salt uptake by an influence upon metabolism. Among those which promote absorption at suitable concentrations are soluble sugars and other respiratory substrates. This effect is most clearly demonstrated in those organisms, for example, bacteria and fungi, which depend on an external supply of carbohydrates for growth. (Pulver and Verzár, 1940; Leibovitz and Kupermintz 1942; Kamen and Spiegelman, 1948) (Fig. 21a). When excised roots, slices of non-green tissues, or photosynthetic organisms in the dark, are depleted of carbohydrate reserves, salt absorption is stimulated by an external supply of sugar. (Hoagland and Broyer, 1936; Helder, 1952). Addition of a number of other organic sub-

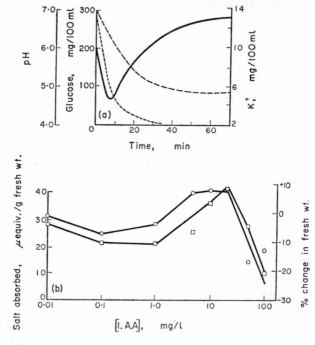

FIG. 21. Effects of glucose [a] and auxin [b] on salt absoprtion
a. Changes with time in the potassium content (—), pH (— — —) and glucose
(----) content of the medium in which *Escherichia coli* cells were suspended
(redrawn from Leibovitz and Kupermintz, 1942); b. Amounts of salt
absorbed (□) and the change in fresh wt. (○) of potato slices placed in
solutions containing salt and various concentrations of indole (3) acetic
acid in 48 hr (redrawn from Commoner and Mazia, 1942).

stances which are essential for growth, for example vitamins and
auxins, to the medium stimulates salt uptake if growth is limited
by these factors (Fig. 21b).

Metabolic inhibitors reduce or entirely suppress active salt
absorption over approximately the same range of concentration as
they inhibit respiration, but absorption of salt is often inhibited
completely at levels which do not entirely prevent oxygen uptake
(Machlis, 1944). 2:4 dinitrophenol and other uncoupling agents
depress salt uptake at certain concentrations but stimulate oxygen
absorption (see Fig. 30, p. 82). Inhibitors of protein synthesis (e.g.
ribonuclease, 8-azaguanine and chloramphenicol) may reduce salt

absorption without any appreciable effect on respiration (see p. 89). An account of the light which the use of inhibitors has shed upon the mechanism of salt absorption is given below.

B. INHERENT FACTORS

1. *Surface–volume Relations*

Since the rate at which salts are transported across surface membranes may be a controlling factor in absorption it is not surprising that uptake tends to be related more closely to surface area than to volume. The problem is presented in its simplest form in cultures of micro-organisms where small cells exhibiting a high surface area to volume ratio absorb salts more rapidly per unit of volume (although not necessarily per unit of surface area) than do large cells. The same relationship holds also between cell volume and a variety of other metabolic activities, including respiration.

When cells are packed together in a tissue, as in a root or storage organ, an additional surface becomes important, namely the surface of the tissue in contact with the external medium. In general, when other things are equal, there is a close relationship between the surface area of a root system in contact with the soil, and the rate of salt absorption. Steward and Harrison (1939) observed a correlation between surface area and absorption of salt in experiments with potato slices of varying thickness (Fig. 22a). In this material, cells near the surface which are in an actively metabolizing and absorbing state represent a greater proportion of the whole number in thin slices than in thick ones, and hence absorption is less active per unit of tissue volume in the latter than in the former.

2. *Internal Salt Concentration*

As the concentration of salt in a tissue rises, absorption occurs more slowly. Hoagland and Broyer (1936) found that roots grown under conditions of minimal nutrient supply (low-salt roots) possess a much greater capacity for subsequent salt absorption than those grown under normal conditions. In non-growing cells of storage tissues, the rate of salt uptake decreases as the internal concentration rises and eventually stops (Fig. 22a). This effect of internal concentration is apparently directly on the absorption mechanism, rather than the result of changes in the rate of passive leakage

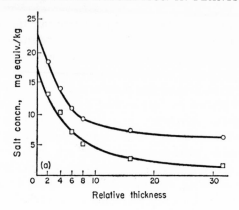

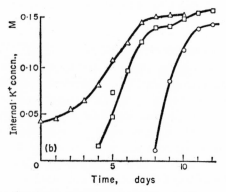

FIG. 22. Effects of disk thickness [a] and internal salt concentration [b] on salt absorption by storage tissue slices

a. Effect of disk thickness on absorption of rubidium and bromide by potato disks in 72 hr at 23 °C. Redrawn from Steward and Harrison (1939); b. Absorption of potassium by red beet root tissue from 0·02 M potassium chloride solutions at 25 °C after preliminary washing in distilled water for a few hours (△—△); 4 days (▢—▢) and 8 days (○—○) (from Sutcliffe, 1952).

(Sutcliffe, 1952). Tissues with high salt content tend to be more turgid than those low in salts and internal concentration may thus exert part of its effect indirectly through an influence on cell turgidity (cf. p. 63).

3. *Internal Sugar Concentration*

The ability of low-salt excised roots to absorb salts rapidly is partly attributable to their high sugar content. If such roots are starved by keeping them for some time in distilled water, their capacity to take up salt diminishes as sugar content falls. Humphries (1956b) demonstrated a positive correlation between the reducing sugar content of excised pea roots and salt uptake. In the same experiments sucrose content seemed either to be unrelated, or to show a negative correlation with absorption. Phillis and Mason (1940) found that cutting off the carbohydrate supply to roots, by ringing, caused reduced absorption of salt in cotton plants. In intact angiosperms, absorption of salt is sometimes depressed with the onset of flowering, and this is correlated with a fall in the level of carbohydrates in the roots. Eaton and Joham (1944) suggested that much of the decline in mineral intake accompanying heavy fruiting in cotton is attributable to reduced movement of carbohydrate to the roots.

4. *Growth*

Although salts can be absorbed rapidly for a limited time by cells which are not growing (see Chapter 2, p. 17), prolonged absorption is closely bound up with a capacity for growth. Mature cells which have irretrievably lost their ability to grow are totally incapable of accumulating ions, while dormant cells which regain a capacity for absorbing salts actively after a period of washing in aerated water, are also capable of further growth.

Growth stimulates the process of salt absorption directly and indirectly in several ways. As a result of growth, there is synthesis of new binding sites and carrier molecules as well as additional incorporation of inorganic ions into insoluble cell constituents. This is particularly important in cells which are actively synthesizing protein and undergoing division. The relationship between salt absorption and protein synthesis is discussed in more detail below (Chapter 5, pp. 88-89). Cell expansion results in increased protoplasmic surface area across which absorption occurs, while the concomitant absorption of water causes a dilution of the vacuolar sap. These changes tend to stimulate salt uptake, especially after growth has been allowed to occur under conditions of salt deficiency (cf. Chapter 2, p. 14). When growth by enlargement slows down, the internal salt concentration tends to rise and absorption decreases. At the same time, metabolism begins to decline and the cells enter either

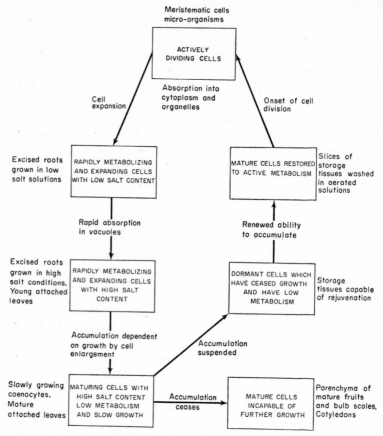

FIG. 23.   Salt accumulation in relation to growth and metabolism (modified from Steward and Sutcliffe, 1959).

a state of senescence or of dormancy. Senescent cells gradually degenerate and release salt to their surroundings, but dormant cells on the other hand can be stimulated to metabolize actively, synthesize protein and absorb salt again under suitable conditions. Some of the relationships between growth at the cell level and salt absorption are summarized diagrammatically in Fig. 23.

There is also a close correlation between growth and the absorption of salt in whole plants. The phase of rapid vegetative growth is accompanied by a marked increase in the amount of

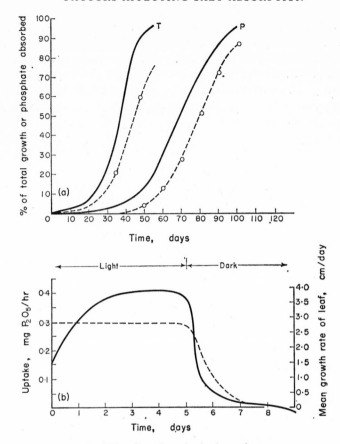

FIG. 24. Growth and salt absorption
a. Growth (○---○) and phosphate absorption (—) in tobacco (T) and potato (P). Redrawn from Dean and Fried (1953); b. Growth (---) and phosphate absorption (—) by maize plants grown at first in light and then transferred to darkness (redrawn from Alberda, 1948).

inorganic elements they contain (Fig. 24a). Any treatment which reduces growth causes a corresponding decrease in the absorption of salts (Fig. 24b). The importance of localized growth in controlling the redistribution of salts within vascular plants, is discussed below (Chapter 7, pp. 125-127).

5. Symbiosis

Root systems of many plants have fungi associated with them to

6   M.S.A.P.

form *mycorrhiza*. There is scattered evidence in the literature that infected plants grow more actively and have a higher ash content than those not infected. Routien and Dawson (1943) suggested that mycorrhizal roots of *Pinus echinata* absorb salts rapidly because the fungus causes stimulation of respiration and additional release of hydrogen ions from the host root for use in exchange reactions with

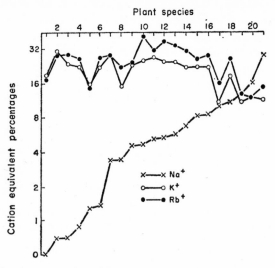

FIG. 25. Amounts of sodium, potassium and rubidium (expressed as percentage of total cation content), in 21 angiosperms, all supplied with the same nutrient medium, containing these elements. Plants: 1. *Fagopyrum*, 2. *Zea*, 3. *Helianthus*, 4. *Chenopodium*, 5. *Salsol*, 6. *Pisum*, 7. *Nicotiana*, 8. *Solanum*, 9. *Spinacia*, 10. *Avena*, 11. *Aster*, 12. *Papaver*, 13. *Lactuca*, 14. *Plantago lanceolata*, 15. *Melilotus*, 16. *Vicia*, 17. *Atriplex littoralis*, 18. *Sinapsis* (*Brassica*), 19. *Salicornia*, 20. *Plantago maritima*, 21. *Atriplex hortensis* (redrawn from Collander, 1941).

the soil (see Chapter 8, pp. 141-2). Another suggestion is that the mycorrhizal fungi produce organic substances which form chelates with inorganic ions in the soil. These complexes may be absorbed by the host root more readily than are free ions (Schatz *et al.* 1954).

6. *Heredity*

Plants differ markedly in the extent to which they absorb particular ions from the same solution as was shown by Newton (1928) and by Collander (1941) (Fig. 25). It is extremely improbable that if any two plants even of the same species were placed under identical conditions, they would each absorb salts in the same proportions or at the same total rate. Individuals of the same clone may be expected to show the smallest differences between one another, while varieties, species and genera show increasing marked contrasts in the pattern of absorption. Species within genera, however, sometimes have features in common; for example, the characteristic accumulation of selenium in species of *Astragalus* referred to above (Chapter 1, p. 4), and of sodium in *Atriplex* spp. (Fig. 25). On the other hand, species of a single genus sometimes differ markedly in the relative amounts of potassium and sodium absorbed from a given environment as is the case in *Plantago lanceolata* and *Plantago maritima* (Fig. 25) and species of *Valonia* (Table 17 B, p. 153). Genetic factors affect not only the sap composition of *Valonia* species in a given environment, but they can also modify the influence exerted by other factors, such as light intensity, upon it (see Chapter 9, pp. 153-4).

For further reading

BROYER, T. C. (1951). The nature of the process of inorganic solute accumulation in roots. In *Mineral Nutrition of Plants* (Ed. E. Truog). (Chap. 8, pp. 187–260). *Univ. of Wisconsin Press.*

EPSTEIN, E. (1956). Uptake and ionic environment (including external pH) *Encycl. Plant Physiol.* II, 398–408.

EPSTEIN, E. (1956b). Mineral Nutrition of Plants: Mechanisms of uptake and transport. *Ann. Rev. Plant Physiol.* 7. 1–24.

KRAMER, P. J. (1956a). The uptake of salts by plant cells. *Encycl. Plant Physiol.* II, 290–315.

STEWARD, F. C. and SUTCLIFFE, J. F. (1959). Plants in relation to inorganic salts. In *Plant Physiology. A Treatise* (Ed. F. C. Steward). (Vol. II.) (pp. 253–478). Academic Press, New York.

CHAPTER 5

SALT ABSORPTION AND
METABOLISM

In all cases osmotic exchanges are correlated and
regulated by the vital activity of the organism. Both
the formation of the plasmatic membranes as well as
any modification of their diosmotic properties which
may later arise are the work of the living organism,
which also initiates those intra- and extracellular
changes to which the continuance of exosmosis and
endosmosis is to be ascribed.

W. PFEFFER.
The Physiology of Plants (1900).

A.   MECHANISM LINKING PASSIVE PROCESSES TO METABOLISM

ALTHOUGH it was known from the beginning of the nineteenth
century that plants discriminate between ions presented to them, the
implication of this fact in relation to the mechanism of absorption
escaped notice for many years. It was not until investigations of
the effects of such factors as temperature and oxygen pressure on
salt uptake were made during the present century that a dependence
of absorption on metabolic energy became widely accepted. Subsequently, analyses of the uncontaminated sap from coenocytes
and giant algal cells showed that salts are accumulated to concentrations higher than those which occur in the medium—a process
which clearly requires expenditure of energy.

Following the recognition that salt absorption and metabolism
are closely connected, various attempts were made to link respiration
to physical mechanisms of ion transport in ways which could
facilitate continuous absorption. If, for example, salts are utilized
or osmotically inactivated within cells, absorption can continue
indefinitely by diffusion through permeable membranes, along
metabolically maintained concentration gradients.

Several schemes have been proposed through which ionic

73

exchange may be linked with metabolism. Brooks (1929) suggested that cations and anions might be absorbed continuously in exchange for ionic products of metabolism. If there is, for instance, a continual production of hydrogen ions inside a cell so that their concentration on one side of a cation-permeable/anion-permeable membrane is maintained at a higher level than on the other side, cations, e.g. potassium ions, can be absorbed against the existing concentration gradient (Fig. 26a). A steady state is reached when the rate of diffusion of hydrogen and potassium ions across the membrane in opposite directions is equal to the rate of production of hydrogen ions in the cell. A similar system can be visualized for

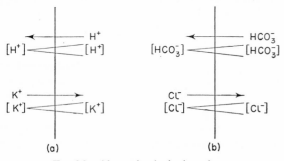

(a)   (b)

FIG. 26.   Absorption by ionic exchange
a. Membrane, cation permeable, anion impermeable. b. Membrane, anion
permeable, cation impermeable.   For explanation, see text;

the accumulation of anions, involving an anion permeable cation-permeable membrane, and metabolically produced anions, such as bicarbonate (Fig. 26b). Brooks supposed that if the surface membrane has a mosaic structure with cation and anion permeable areas, the two systems may be combined, and by simultaneous production of hydrogen and bicarbonate ions, accumulation of a neutral salt be achieved. Sollner (1932) pointed out that such a mechanism will not function unless the cation and anion permeable regions are electrically insulated from one another. More recently, he devised a model system in which this condition is met (Sollner, 1955), and simultaneous accumulation of anions and cations by exchange was demonstrated. Conceivably anions and cations might be accumulated initially into separate electrically insulated compartments in the cytoplasm of plant cells, and subsequently mixed in the vacuoles, but there is no evidence at present that this occurs. Briggs (1932) suggested that cations and anions might be accumulated separately in distinct phases of the cell—for example, cations in the cytoplasm and anions in vacuoles. While it is true that an excess of mobile cations over mobile anions is maintained in cytoplasm by the establishment of Donnan equilibria, the fact that both anions and cations are accumulated in vacuoles renders this hypothesis inadequate to account for one of the most characteristic features of salt absorption in plants.

Continuous uptake by adsorption can be linked with metabolism either through synthesis of new adsorption sites during growth, or by vacation of occupied sites as a result of metabolic utilization of ions. The clearest examples of labile, metabolism-dependent, binding of cations are derived from work with micro-organisms. Pulver and Verzár (1940) observed that when yeast cells were placed in a potassium-free medium, about one-third of the potassium diffused out rapidly. Upon subsequent incubation with glucose, the ions were reabsorbed during a brief period in which glucose was taken up (cf. Fig. 21a, p. 64). Cowie *et al.* (1949) suggested that in *Escherichia coli* intermediates of sugar breakdown, perhaps glucose-6-phosphate and fructose-6-phosphate, may be involved as binding substances.

B. Active Transport

1. *Acid–base Carriers*

None of the above mechanisms is adequate to explain the rapid transport of ions from one side to another of a membrane with a high resistance to passive penetration. Where such membranes are present carrier mechanisms are usually invoked (see Chapter 3, pp. 40-41). In general, metabolism might be involved in:

(*a*) the synthesis of carrier molecules,

(*b*) complex formation between the ion and its carrier,

(*c*) transport of the ion-carrier complex,

(*d*) breakdown of the complex, or

(*e*) the movement of the unloaded carrier back to the outer surface of the membrane.

One of the first precise mechanisms proposed for active transport of cations was that suggested by Osterhout (1936) from observations with *Valonia*. He proposed that an acidic substance (HX) located in the outer protoplasmic membrane combines with an entering base according to the equation

$$KOH + HX \rightarrow KX + H_2O$$

The neutral, undissociated complex (KX) diffuses across the protoplasm and is decomposed at the inner surface where the sap is more acid than the external medium (cf. Fig. 11b, p. 40). The necessary pH gradient might be maintained by production of carbon dioxide in respiration. The failure of *Valonia* to absorb sodium as rapidly as potassium by this mechanism was attributed to the lower mobility of the sodium ion-carrier complex in the membrane.

Various objections can be raised to Osterhout's hypothesis:

(*a*) It is difficult to adapt the mechanism satisfactorily to account for the simultaneous accumulation of anions and cations in vacuoles.

(*b*) Excised roots can accumulate cations when the medium is more acid than the cell sap (see p. 55);

(*c*) absorption seems to be more closely related to oxygen absorption than carbon dioxide production, since absorption stops in higher plant cells under anaerobic conditions, whereas carbon dioxide production does not;

(*d*) absorption sometimes occurs more efficiently than is expected on the basis of the 1 : 1 exchange of cations and carbon dioxide postulated (see p. 80).

Jacobson and Overstreet (1947) enunciated a general mechanism for active transport involving acidic and basic carrier molecules for cations and anions respectively, which avoids some of the objections to Osterhout's hypothesis. They suggested that ions combine with unspecified carrier molecules (HX, YOH) in the cell membrane, according to the equations:

$$M^+ + HX \rightleftharpoons MX + H^+$$
$$A^- + YOH \rightleftharpoons YA + OH^-$$

These reversible reactions are thought to be involved both in the uptake of ions on one side of the membrane and their release on the other. The carriers are presumed to be synthesized metabolically and to combine electrostatically with ions, but no specific mechanism is proposed for subsequent decomposition of the complex so formed. The view that the cation carrier is acidic is based on the observation that hydrogen ions compete with other cations for the absorption mechanism (see p. 55). Comparable competition between hydroxyl and other anions has also been claimed.

2. Electro-chemical Hypotheses

a. The Lundegårdh hypothesis. Some of the early investigators, notably Hoagland and Steward, while recognizing a general

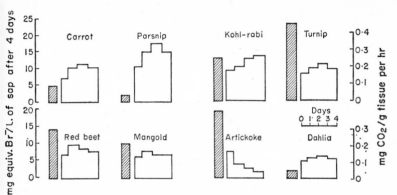

FIG. 27. Ion absorption and respiration. Bromide absorption (shaded rectangles) and carbon dioxide production in 4 days by slices of various storage tissues (Berry and Steward, 1934).

dependence of salt uptake on respiration, could not demonstrate a quantitative relationship between the two processes. The rate at which a storage tissue respires, for example, is a poor guide to the rate at which it absorbs salts (Fig. 27). Lundegårdh and Burström (1933) contended, however, that an exact quantitative correlation exists between anion absorption and a particular component of respiration which is stimulated by salt, and is called "anion" or "salt" respiration, in contrast to a basal or "ground" respiration which is unrelated to uptake of salt (Fig. 28, a, b). In the presence of cyanide at an appropriate concentration (0·0001M HCN), salt uptake and salt respiration are completely inhibited, without any apparent effect on "ground" respiration (Fig. 28b). This fact led Lundegårdh (1939) to propose that anion respiration is mediated through cytochrome

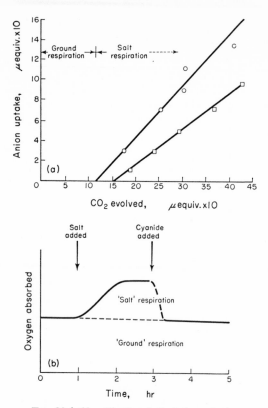

FIG. 28 (a-b). The Lundegårdh hypothesis
a. Relationship between anion uptake and respiration in wheat roots placed in solutions containing various concentrations of potassium nitrate (○) and potassium chloride (□) (redrawn from Lundegårdh and Burström, 1933); b. Effects of salt and cyanide on oxygen absorption by disks of storage tissue (based on data of Robertson and Turner, 1945).

oxidase and further to suggest that cytochrome may be the carrier for anions. Additional support for these ideas was provided by the observation that absorption and salt respiration are inhibited by a more specific inhibitor of cytochrome oxidase than cyanide, namely carbon monoxide in the dark. Some details of the mechanism proposed by Lundegårdh as it is now conceived are shown in Fig. 28c. It is postulated that an oxidation-reduction potential gradient exists across the functional membrane, such that cytochrome molecules tend to become oxidized at the outer surface, and reduced

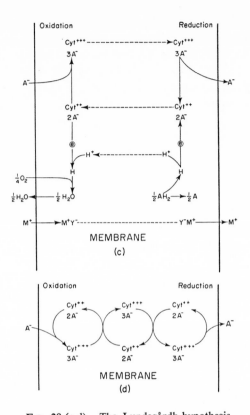

FIG. 28 (c-d). The Lundegårdh hypothesis.
c. Diagrammatic representation of the Lundegårdh hypothesis. (For explanation see text); d. Anion transport involving a chain of cytochrome molecules.

on the inside. The gradient might depend on differences of oxygen pressure on the two sides, or on the spatial location of enzymes. Cytochrome is presumed either to be freely diffusible within the membrane or to vibrate from one position to another, so that it becomes alternately oxidized and reduced. Anions are taken up when cytochrome becomes oxidized at the outer surface and released when it becomes reduced at the inner surface because of the ability of an oxidized cytochrome molecule to bind one more anion than can a reduced molecule. Transport of anions across thin membranes might be achieved in a single step, or, alternatively, anions might be handed on from one cytochrome molecule to another in traversing greater distances (Fig. 28d).

According to the Lundegårdh hypothesis, the transport of anions inwards across a membrane is accompanied by movement of an equivalent number of electrons and hydrogen ions outwards. These are derived from reduced respiratory intermediates, and subsequently combine with molecular oxygen to produce water, the final product of respiration. The maximum number of anions transported by such a mechanism per oxygen molecule consumed in salt respiration is 4, since 4 electrons are utilized in the reduction of a molecule of oxygen to water, and one anion is absorbed per electron transferred. With wheat roots, the ratio observed is commonly less than 1, but Robertson and Wilkins (1948) found with slices of carrot tissue that the ratio approached but did not apparently exceed 4 when the concentration of salts in the medium was increased (Fig. 29). This was taken to indicate that the Lundegårdh mechanism probably operates in plants.

Cations are thought to be absorbed passively along "adsorption tracks" under the influence of an electrical gradient created by the absorption of anions (cf. mechanism d, Fig. 13, p. 44). This contention is supported by the lack of a quantitative relationship between respiration and the absorption of cations.

Most investigators have found it impossible to accept the Lundegårdh hypothesis for various reasons of which the following are perhaps the most important:

(a) If a single type of carrier molecule is involved in the uptake of all anions, anions should compete with one another for the absorption mechanism when they are supplied simultaneously. In fact, competition occurs between closely related ions such as chloride and bromide, but not between halides, sulphate, nitrate or phosphate (see p. 58). Lundegårdh (1955) admitted that cytochrome is unlikely to be the carrier for metabolically important ions, which in effect confines the hypothesis to a mechanism for absorption of chloride. It must be pointed out that nitrate absorption bore a similar relationship to anion respiration as did chloride uptake in the experiments upon which the hypothesis was originally based (Fig. 28a) and if it is now denied that cytochrome acts as a carrier

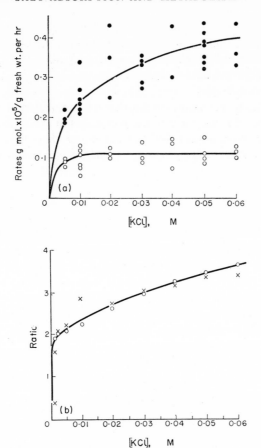

FIG. 29. Salt absorption and respiration

a. Rates of salt absorption (●) and salt respiration (○) by carrot tissue placed in solutions of potassium chloride (redrawn from Robertson and Wilkins, 1948); b. Values of the ratio $\dfrac{\text{salt absorbed (gm. mol.)}}{\text{salt respiration (gm. mol.)}}$ for carrot tissue placed in solutions of potassium chloride. Calculated from the data of Fig. 29a. (redrawn from Robertson and Wilkins 1948).

for nitrate, it may well be asked what reason there is for believing that it functions in the case of chloride either.

(b) There are cases in which salt uptake is apparently linked to other oxidases than cytochrome, for example, ascorbic acid oxidase (Russell, 1954). Ascorbic acid oxidase seems to mediate part of the electron transport in barley roots and could conceivably function as an ion carrier in a basically similar manner to cytochrome. In anaerobic organisms, electron transport and anion absorption must obviously be linked to other systems than that involving cytochromes and oxygen.

(c) It is by no means certain that the stimulation of respiration caused by salt is due more to the presence of anions than of cations. Hoagland and Steward (1939) pointed out that the ions having greatest effects on respiration in their experiments were those

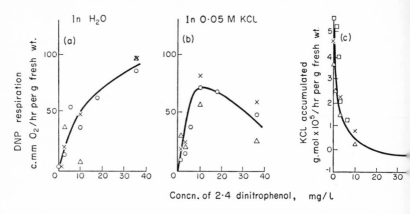

FIG. 30.   Salt absorption and respiration. Relationship between concentration of dinitrophenol (DNP) and a-b, the rate of DNP respiration (i.e. the rate of O_2 absorption in DNP over that in water or salt), and c, the amount of KCl accumulated in carrot tissue; X, O, and △—disks from one batch of carrots, respectively 144, 264 and 312 hr after cutting: ⊡ from another batch of carrots, 96 hr from cutting (redrawn from Robertson, Wilkins and Weeks, 1951).

containing nitrogen, i.e. an anion (NO_3^-) and a cation (NH_4^+). Epstein (1954) demonstrated that salt respiration is stimulated in the presence of a cation exchange resin from which anions are not absorbed.

(d) The Lundegårdh hypothesis rests on the establishment of a quantitative relationship between cyanide-sensitive respiration and anion uptake. Some discrepancies between the two processes were noted by Lundegårdh (1940), but not emphasised unduly. Strong evidence against the hypothesis was supplied by the observation of Robertson et al. (1951) that 2:4 dinitrophenol (DNP), at certain concentrations, inhibits salt uptake but stimulates cyanide-sensitive respiration (Fig. 30). Lundegårdh (1954) explained, however, that only one of the cytochrome components (cytochrome b) may be involved in salt uptake and this is inactivated by inhibitors of phosphorylation, while cyanide-sensitive respiration continues through other cytochromes by-passing cytochrome b. He observed spectrophotometrically that cytochromes a and c continue to function whereas b remains oxidized when wheat roots are immersed

TABLE 7. THE RATIOS SODIUM ABSORBED METABOLICALLY/OXYGEN INVOLVED IN SALT RESPIRATION FOR WASHED SLICES OF RED BEET TISSUE PLACED IN SOLUTIONS OF SODIUM CHLORIDE AND SODIUM BICARBONATE.

Metabolic absorption was estimated as the difference between uptake at the high temperature (15 °C, or 25 °C) and at a low temperature (1–2 °C.). Salt respiration was estimated as the difference between rates of oxygen absorption in distilled water and in salt solution, at the high temperatures.
(Sutcliffe, unpublished).

Salt	Conc. (M)	Temp. (° C)	Duration of absorption period (hr.)					
			1	2	3	4	5	6
NaCl	0·01	15	5·1	5·1	4·5	4·5	4·0	4·0
	0·01	25	6·3	5·2	4·5	3·7	3·3	3·3
	0·04	25	6·5	5·3	5·0	4·8	4·3	4·0
NaHCO$_3$	0·01	15	8·5	7·9	6·7	6·7	6·1	6·1
	0·01	25	14·0	10·4	8·4	7·3	6·1	6·1
	0·04	25	14·8	10·1	8·5	7·3	7·0	6·6

in DNP at a concentration of 3×10^{-5}M. Inhibitors of protein synthesis may block ion absorption without any apparent effect on respiration (see pp. 88-9), but a detailed study of the possible influence such substances have on the cytochromes has yet to be made.

(e) The maximum number of anions transported for each molecule of oxygen consumed in salt respiration is 4 on the basis of the Lundegårdh hypothesis. However, evidence has now been obtained with both plant and animal tissues that under favourable conditions more than 4 ion pairs may be transported per oxygen molecule consumed (see Sutcliffe and Hackett, 1957, also Table 7). If this is true, an electrochemical mechanism must be at least supplemented by another of higher efficiency.

(f) As Russell (1954) pointed out, the theory of Lundegårdh denies the possibility that cells can store an ability to absorb salts as a result of prior respiration. He obtained evidence that previous respiration facilitates the subsequent movement of phosphate into barley roots under conditions of reduced metabolism. Ketchum (1939) suggested that dark-induced uptake of phosphatc in phosphate-deficient cells of *Nitzschia closterium* exposed previously to light, might be due to combination between the ion and phosphate-binding substances synthesized in light. Lowenhaupt (1956) found similarly that *Potomogeton* leaves will take up extra calcium ions in the dark, following exposure of the leaf to light in the absence of calcium.

Laties (1959) has shown that when potato slices are transferred from a high temperature in the absence of salt to salt at 0 °C, uptake of chloride proceeds quite rapidly at first, and only gradually falls. He suggested that this may be attributed to the presence of a "carrier precursor", which is synthesized at high temperature, and gradually consumed at 0 °C.

(g) The high selectivity of cation uptake in many plants seems unlikely if a passive mechanism of absorption such as that visualized by Lundegårdh is operative. Although it is not impossible that preference exhibited by the binding substances (Y^- Fig. 28c) could be responsible for some discrimination between cations, it is unlikely that this could account for the extreme specificity of cation absorption which is observed.

(h) Cation absorption seems to occur to a large extent independently of anion absorption in some plants, notably in yeast, and in some marine algae.

b. The redox pump. Conway (1953, 1955) proposed an electrochemical mechanism for the transport of cations in muscle cells and yeast which resembles in certain respects that proposed by Lundegårdh for anions. It is suggested that ions (M^+) become bound to a reduced respiratory intermediate (X^-) in accordance with the equation:

$$X^- + M^+ \rightarrow XM$$

The uncharged complex so formed diffuses across the cell membrane and becomes oxidized by transferring an electron (e) to another oxidized substance (A) with release of the ion thus

(i) $XM \rightarrow X + M^+ + (e)$

(ii) $\frac{1}{2}A + (e) + H^+ \rightarrow \frac{1}{2}AH_2$

The oxidized carrier X returns across the membrane and becomes reduced to reform the active carrier according to the equation:

$$\frac{1}{2}AH_2 + X \rightarrow X^- + H^+ + \frac{1}{2}A$$

Under aerobic conditions, hydrogen ions combine with oxygen and electrons to produce water; other hydrogen acceptors may be implicated under anaerobic conditions.

It should be noted that in contrast to the Lundegårdh hypothesis, the redox pump will transport ions from a more reducing to a less reducing region of the cell membrane. It is therefore an especially appropriate mechanism for transporting cations in the outward direction from cells, as occurs, for example, in yeast, certain sea-weeds, and animal tissues. Active excretion of a particular cation for example, sodium, might be accompanied by either active or passive absorption of another cation such as potassium, and it could be in such a way that the low sodium and high potassium content of certain plant and animal tissues is maintained (see Chapter 9, p. 154). Conway suggested that uptake of alkali cations may be achieved also by exchange for hydrogen ions actively excreted by the redox pump. Anion transport is excluded from Conway's scheme since, if exchange of cations occurs there is no net transfer of positive charges. Anion accumulation must therefore depend on a separate mechanism, involving either anion exchange, or con-comitant net absorption of cations.

The redox pump is more acceptable than Lundegårdh's hypothesis in that it is not so rigidly linked to a particular carrier molecule. It could operate in anaerobic as well as aerobic organisms and it accounts more adequately for the selective absorption of cations. It is unsatisfactory in explaining the simultaneous absorp-tion of cations and anions and in its simple form it suffers from the same limitation of efficiency as the Lundegårdh mechanism.

3. Phosphorylation Mechanisms

a. General. In view of the increasing amount of evidence that "energy-rich" organic phosphates such as adenosine triphosphate act as intermediates in energy transfer, it seems not unreasonable to conclude that active transport, like other endergonic processes, depends on energy derived more or less directly from such substances. The effects of phosphorylation inhibitors, such as dinitrophenol, on salt absorption support this conclusion.

The efficiency of active transport by a phosphorylation mechanism is not limited to the same maximum value as are electro-chemical hypotheses. On the assumption that the energy from one "high-energy" phosphate group ($\sim$P) is utilized in the transport of one ion pair and that a net $38 \sim$P are produced in the complete oxidation of 1 molecule of glucose, the maximum value for the ratio of ion pairs absorbed to oxygen involved $\simeq 6\cdot3$. In fact, values of up to about 18 have been observed under some conditions with both animal and plant material, which suggests that at least three ion pairs may in certain circumstances be transported per $\sim$P utilized.

The precise manner in which phosphate group energy might be utilized in active transport remains to be elucidated. Several hypotheses have been proposed of which two are illustrated in Fig. 31 (see also Fig. 12 d; e p. 43), but none of them has yet received convincing experimental support. Evidence indicating a close relationship between ATP-energized protein turnover and salt absorption is presented below (pp. 88-9).

b. Phosphate absorption. Particular interest attaches to the uptake of phosphate by plants because of its unique function in metabolism. There is a large amount of evidence, from a variety of micro-organisms and higher plants, that absorption is closely related to metabolic utilization. A number of reactions are known in which inorganic phosphate is esterified during the course of metabolism, for example, in the synthesis of glucose-1-phosphate during the breakdown of starch by phosphorylase, and in the conversion of 3-phosphoglyceraldehyde to 1:3-diphosphoglyceric acid during glycolysis. The nucleotides, adenosine di- and tri-phosphate are also implicated in phosphate binding. During electron transport, ADP is converted to ATP with utilization of energy and absorption of inorganic phosphate. Gourley (1952) found that radioactivity from ^{32}P-labelled phosphate enters the ATP in red blood cells faster than it reaches inorganic phosphate, and suggested that phosphate may be transported as ATP. Loughman and Russell (1957) showed similarly that phosphate is transferred

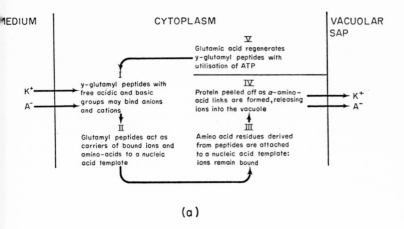

(a)

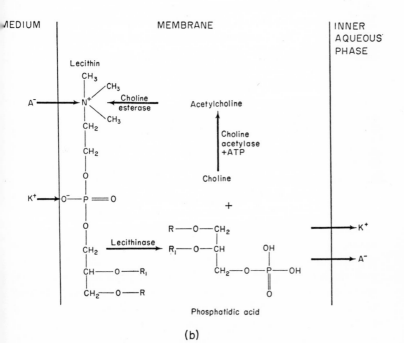

(b)

Fig. 31.   Carrier mechanisms in which ATP is implicated
a. A mechanism linking salt uptake to protein synthesis (redrawn from
Steward and Millar, 1954); b. A cyclic mechanism of active transport involving
lecithin as an amphoteric carrier (redrawn from Bennet-Clark, 1956).

rapidly to ATP in barley roots and only later appears in hexose phosphates and nucleic acids. While it is clear that phosphate became bound, at first temporarily, and later permanently, into cell constituents as a result of metabolic processes, the relationship between these reactions and absorption remain unclear. Phosphate either diffuses passively to the sites of binding which may be at or near the surface of the cytoplasm, or it is transported actively by a carrier mechanism across an impermeable membrane before reaching the metabolic sites. If the latter situation obtains the nature of the specific carrier substances and their relationship to intermediates of phosphate metabolism need to be elucidated. Mitchell (1957) has proposed that transport of phosphate across the surface membrane in bacteria depends upon a specific enzyme-like protein (a "translocase") located in the membrane, which is capable of combining with phosphate on one side and releasing it on the other. The mechanism may either facilitate phosphate exchange, or cause accumulation, depending upon the rate of transfer of ions in the reverse direction.

c. Active transport and protein synthesis.

From his investigations of the factors affecting protein synthesis and salt absorption in storage tissues, Steward was led to conclude that a close relationship exists between the two processes. In an attempt to explain this correlation, Steward and Street (1947) suggested that a precursor of protein combines with both anions and cations at the surface of protoplasm, and functions as an amphoteric carrier. Within the cytoplasm, the carrier is utilized and the ions are released to diffuse passively into the vacuole. This hypothesis was further elaborated by Steward and Millar (1954) to implicate nucleic acids in the mechanisms of protein synthesis and salt absorption (Fig. 31a).

It has been pointed out that ions can be accumulated in cells in the absence of net protein synthesis or even when protein hydrolysis is occurring (Ulrich, 1941; Humphries, 1951). However, the breakdown and resynthesis of protein (protein turnover) is probably a constant feature of living protoplasm, and it is not impossible that this process could mediate active transport even in the absence of net synthesis. The observation that accumulation is prevented by chloramphenicol, a specific inhibitor of protein synthesis, at concentrations which do not affect oxygen absorption (Fig. 32a) supports the view that active transport is more closely linked to protein synthesis than to some other aspects of metabolism. Chloramphenicol, at the concentrations used, did not interfere with protoplasmic streaming in red beet or *Elodea* cells and since streaming probably depends on the folding and unfolding of protein chains it is unlikely that salt absorption occurs by a mechanism such as that

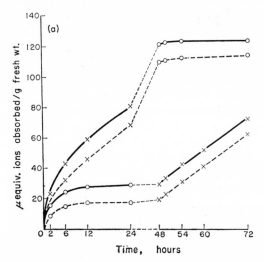

FIG. 32 (a).   Effect of chloramphenicol on salt absorption
a. Uptake of sodium ions (—) and chloride (---) from 0·01 M sodium chloride (+) and 0·01 M sodium chloride plus chloramphenicol (2g per l.) (○) by washed red beet tissue at 25 °C. After 48 hr, the disks were transferred to alternative media as indicated (from Sutcliffe, 1960);

proposed by Goldacre and Lorch (1950) (Fig. 12d, p. 43). It is more likely to be related to a cycle of ion binding and release accompanying the synthesis and hydrolysis of protein (cf. Fig. 31a). In this case, salt transport may be a general property of protein associated with membranes. Membrane synthesis, folding and vesiculation may be involved in transferring the ion–protein complexes from place to place, within the cytoplasm, and in depositing the free ions finally within vacuoles (Fig. 12 e, p. 43; see also Chapters 6 and 10).

A feature of cells of storage tissues is that when first cut from the dormant organ they are incapable of accumulating salt actively, but a capacity to do so develops if they are washed for a time in an aerated solution of salt or in aerated distilled water (see Fig. 4 p. 16, and Fig. 22b, p. 66). The development of absorptive ability has been attributed to synthesis or activation of carrier molecules resulting from enhanced metabolism induced by this treatment (Sutcliffe, 1954b). It has been observed (Fig. 32b) that chloramphenicol inhibits this process, and disks washed for 48 hr in a

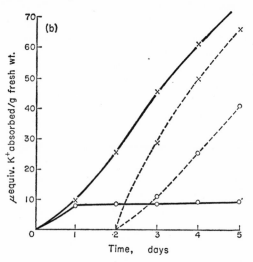

FIG. 32 (b).   Effect of chloramphenicol on salt absorption
b. Uptake of potassium ions by red beet disks, washed for about a day in water, and then transferred (a) to 0·01 M potassium chloride (+—+) (b) to distilled water for 2 days, and then 0·01 M potassium chloride (+---+) (c) to 0·01 M potassium chloride+chloramphenicol (2g per l) (○—○) and (a) to chloramphenicol (2g per l) for 2 days, and then transferred to 0·01 M potassium chloride, at 25 °C (from Sutcliffe, 1960).

solution of the antibiotic behave as if they are freshly cut. The respiration rate is lower than that of similar disks washed in water, and chloramphenicol evidently inhibits some metabolic activity (perhaps the synthesis of protein), upon which both enhanced respiration and the stimulation of ion absorption depend.

C.   SALT ABSORPTION AND ORGANIC ACID METABOLISM

Hoagland and Broyer (1936) noticed that after barley roots had absorbed salt from a solution of calcium bromide, the expressed sap was less well buffered than it was following uptake of potassium bromide, and they suggested that the organic acid content of roots might be different after the two treatments. Ulrich (1941) confirmed that when cations are absorbed in excess of anions (e.g. from a solution of potassium sulphate), organic acid anions appear in the sap (cf. Chapter 4, p. 52). Conversely, when an excess of anions are absorbed (e.g. from a solution of calcium bromide), the organic acid content decreases. In Ulrich's experiments there was an approximate agreement between the excess absorption of one ion and the change in organic acid content, except during absorption from solutions of calcium nitrate. Here, the excess of anions over cations absorbed was presumably balanced by loss of other anions, e.g. hydroxyl or bicarbonate. Ulrich suggested that it is the unequal absorption of anions and cations which in some way induces changes in organic acid content to maintain electrical neutrality, whereas Lundegårdh (1954) proposed that synthesis or disappearance or organic acid anions (i.e. of negatively charged particles) may be the cause of unequal cation and anion absorption, since it stimulates or retards absorption of cations along an electrical gradient.

It must be emphasized at this point that the normal operation of the Krebs cycle does not result in accumulation of organic acids; rather this is achieved through carbon dioxide or bicarbonate fixation linked with the cycle. It seems probable that depending on external conditions, e.g. pH and the tissue under investigation, either carbon dioxide or bicarbonate ions are taken up and converted to organic acid anions, which balance part of the cations absorbed. In the case of carbon dioxide fixation, the excess of absorbed cations over anions is replaced in the medium by an equivalent number of hydrogen ions. When bicarbonate is absorbed, equal numbers of positive and negative charges are transported, and no exchange occurs. It is possible that if bicarbonate is taken up as such, it is converted to carbon dioxide at the pH of cell sap before incorporation in organic acid. The various possibilities are represented diagrammatically in Fig. 33. Most of the organic acid anions ($OA.^-$) in cells are located in vacuoles, into which they are transferred, together with mobile cations from cytoplasm where they are synthetized.

When excess absorption of anions over cations is observed, there is sometimes a reduction in the organic acid content of the cells, and this is accompanied by an increased respiratory quotient. The mechanisms involved here are presumably the reverse of those just discussed, namely carbon dioxide or bicarbonate release from organic acid, accompanied by a decrease in the hydrogen ion concentration of the medium.

Further evidence that organic acid metabolism and salt absorption are linked has been obtained by experiments involving Krebs cycle inhibitors. Machlis (1944) observed that iodoacetate and

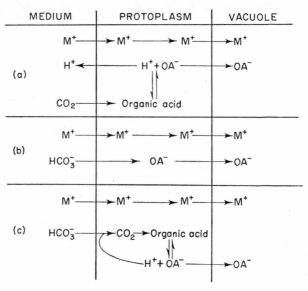

FIG. 33. Organic acid metabolism and cation absorption. For explanation, see text.

malonate inhibit both salt absorption and respiration in barley roots. The effects of iodoacetate were reversed completely by adding malate, succinate or fumarate, and those of malonate were partially reversed by these acids. Ordin and Jacobson (1955) confirmed that pretreatment of barley roots with various inhibitors of the Krebs cycle enzymes prevents ion absorption without entirely suppressing respiration. They concluded that the Krebs cycle and phosphorylation control the synthesis of ion-carriers, while cytochrome oxidase functions in salt uptake by facilitating energy release through metabolism.

For further reading

Burström, H. (1951). The mechanism of ion absorption. In *Mineral Nutrition of Plants*. (Ed. E. Truog). (pp. 251–60). Univ. of Wisconsin Press.

Kramer, P. J. (1956). Permeability in relation to respiration. *Encycl. Plant Physiol.* 2, 358–68.

Laties, G. C. (1959). Active transport of salt into plant tissue. *Ann. Rev. Plant Physiol.* 10, 87–112.

Lundegårdh, H. (1954). Anion respiration. *Symp. Soc. Exp. Biol.* 8, 262–96.

Lundegårdh, H. (1955). Mechanisms of absorption, transport, accumulation and secretion of ions. *Ann. Rev. Plant Physiol.* 6, 1–24.

Robertson, R. N. (1960). Ion transport and respiration. *Biol. Rev.* 35, 231–64.

Steward, F. C. (1937). Salt accumulation by plants—the role of growth and metabolism. *Trans. Faraday Soc.* 33, 1006–16.

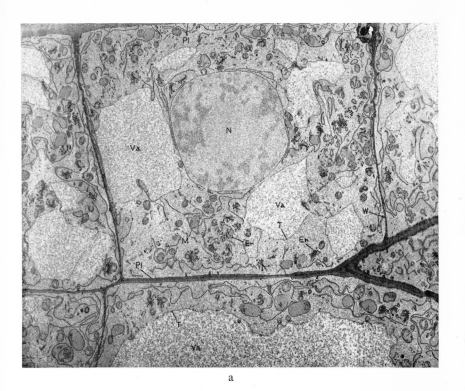

a

PLATE I.   The ultrastructure of plant cells

a. Electron micrograph showing the structure of cytoplasm in maize (*Zea mays*) root cells at a distance of 1–1·5 mm from the root tip. Fixation was with potassium permanganate which accentuates membranes. Invagination of the plasmalemma can be seen, and also some parts of the endoplasmic reticulum. The central vacuole of a mature cell arises by coalescence of smaller vacuoles. Magnification 2,025× (Photograph reproduced by courtesy of W. G. Whaley and H. J. Mollenhauer).

Key: N=nucleus; Va=vacuole; V=cytoplasmic vesicle (not clearly distinguishable in a); W=cellulose cell wall; Pl=plasmalemma; T=tonoplast (not clearly distinguishable in b); Er=endoplasmic reticulum; g=small dense granule (ribonucleoprotein particle).

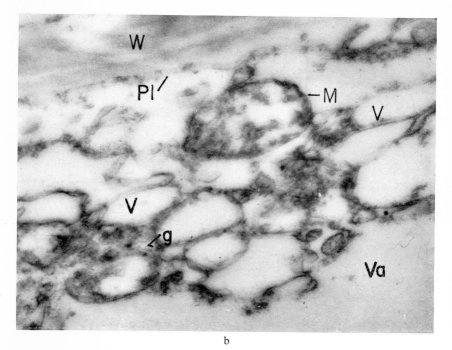

b

PLATE I. (cont.) The ultrastructure of plant cells.

b. Electron micrograph showing the structure of cytoplasm in a mature cortical cell located about 2mm from the tip of a maize (*Zea mays*) root. Fixation with osmium in veronal buffer. The most prominent feature is the presence of numerous large vesicles. The plasmalemma seems to be continuous with membranes surrounding the vesicles. Magnification, 36,000 × (Photograph reproduced from Lund, Vatter and Hanson (1958) by courtesy of the authors).

Key: N=nucleus; Va=vacuole; V=cytoplasmic vesicle (not clearly distinguishable in a); W=cellulose cell wall; Pl=plasmalemma; T=tonoplast (not clearly distinguishable in b); Er=endoplasmic reticulum; g=small dense granule (ribonucleoprotein particle).

CHAPTER 6

STRUCTURAL ASPECTS OF SALT ABSORPTION IN CELLS

When new appearance is before the eyes,
New suppositions thereupon arise.
C. MORTON (1687).

A. LOCATION OF ABSORPTION MECHANISMS

1. *Early Observations*

Early investigators of ion absorption viewed the cytoplasm simply as a membrane across which transport into the central vacuole occurs. Thus, they disregarded the morphological complexity of protoplasm (Plate I) and ignored the possibility that salts may be accumulated within it. Briggs (1932) was among the first to call attention to the retention of ions in cytoplasm, and later it became possible to investigate the situation experimentally using algae with large cells. Brooks (1940) immersed *Nitella* plants in salt solutions containing radioactive isotopes of alkali metals for varying lengths of time and then determined the radioactivity of cellulose walls, protoplasm and vacuolar sap separately. The wall fraction attained an apparent concentration of salt similar to that of the medium immediately upon immersion, and a few minutes later the concentration of radioactive ions in the protoplasm was several times higher than that of the medium. Entry into the vacuolar sap proceeded rather slowly and little or no radioactivity was detected there several hours after immersion (Fig. 34a). Similar results were obtained in experiments with radioactive bromide (^{82}Br). Hoagland and Broyer (1942) confirmed the rapid movement of ions from the medium into the protoplasm of *Nitella* and its slow transference into the sap. In contrast to Brooks, they found that when the experimental period was prolonged, the apparent con-

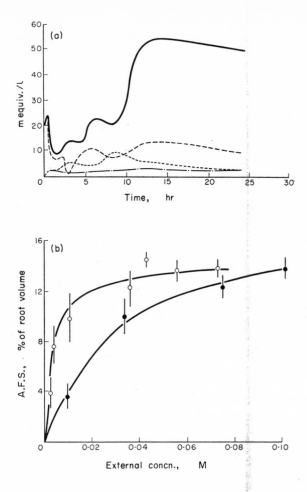

FIG. 34. a. Concentrations of sodium (—,---) and bromide (---, —·—·—)
in the protoplasm (——,---) and sap (---,—·—·) of *Nitella* after immersion in
0·01 M sodium chloride labelled with radioactive sodium, and 0·01 M sodium
bromide labelled with radioactive bromide for 24 hr (redrawn from Brooks,
1940); b. Relationship between the apparent free space of bean root tissue and
the external concentration of potassium chloride. Points plotted are means
and standard deviations of experimental results and the full lines represent the
theoretical relationship between AFS and external concentration based on
the establishment of Donnan equilibria ○—○ = 5 mm of root apex; ●—● =
section of root 2–3 cm from the apex (redrawn from Hope, 1953).

centration of salt in the sap eventually exceeded that in the protoplasm if the plants were kept under aerobic conditions. In the
absence of oxygen, salts appeared to move into protoplasm but not
into the sap, leading Hoagland and Broyer to the conclusion that
active transport occurs from the protoplasm into the vacuole, and
uptake into protoplasm may take place passively.

2. *Apparent Free Space*

Attempts have been made to determine more exactly the location
of permeability barriers in plant cells by estimating the volume of a
tissue which is passively penetrated by salts or organic solutes.
The principle of the method is as follows: if an unknown quantity of
water is added to a known amount of an aqueous solution of known
concentration, the volume of water added can be calculated from a
measurement of the change in concentration. Similarly, if a piece of
tissue is placed in a given volume of solution of known concentration,
under conditions which inhibit metabolism, the volume of tissue
penetrated passively can be calculated on the assumption that the
concentration of solute attained in this region is the same as that
in the external medium. To the space within a tissue into which
salts move passively to a concentration equalling that of the medium,
the terms "water-free space" (WFS) and "outer space" have been
applied.

The method was used successfully by Conway and Downey
(1950) with yeast, and they calculated that about 26 per cent of the
volume of a packed cell suspension is penetrated passively by
inulin, gelatin and peptone. This volume is close to the theoretical
space between closely packed spheres of the size of yeast plants,
suggesting that these substances do not enter the cells at an appreciable rate. The volume of yeast suspension penetrated by some other
substances, including potassium and sodium chlorides, was found
to be 33–34 per cent of the total, and the additional volume was
identified as water-filled spaces in wet cell walls. In yeast, therefore,
it seems that there is a barrier to diffusion and exchange of ions at
the outer surface of the protoplasm, immediately within the cell
wall. Using the same technique, Mitchell (1954) established that a
barrier to diffusion of phosphate is present, at or near, the surface
of the protoplasm of *Staphylococcus* cells.

Cowie *et al.* (1949) concluded, on the contrary, that the outer cytoplasmic surface in *Escherichia coli* is freely permeable to sodium and potassium ions. The amount of sodium entering cells transferred from distilled water to a solution of salt was found to be about equal to that predicted on the assumption that equality of concentration inside and outside the cell was attained; no metabolic control of sodium uptake was observed. A similar, freely diffusible component of potassium absorption was demonstrated, but in addition a considerable metabolic binding of potassium ions to cell constituents occurred. Unbound sodium and potassium was rapidly lost to the medium when cells were placed in distilled water; bound potassium was also lost, but at a much slower rate. Cowie *et al.* (1950) found that sulphate is taken up passively by resting cells of *Escherichia coli* into a water-free space occupying 75 per cent of the cell volume. Negligible metabolic binding occurred, as was shown by the ease with which the sulphate absorbed was subsequently washed out again. In growing cells, on the other hand, sulphate becomes incorporated into organic substances to an extent which is pro-portional to the increase in cell mass. In contrast to passive penetration, metabolic incorporation of sulphate depends on the presence of glucose, and a nitrogen source; and it is affected by temperature and aeration. A yeast, *Torulopsis utilis*, was found to differ from *Escherichia coli* by its ability to incorporate sulphate into organic sulphur compounds even without growth. A water-free space was detected comparable to that found in the bacterium. Similar experiments with phosphate indicated that in both *Escherichia coli* and *Torulopsis utilis*, passive penetration occurs into a free space which occupies an appreciable part of the cell volume, and metabolic incorporation takes place, even under conditions which do not permit growth.

There is evidently as yet no general agreement on the passive permeability of the outer cytoplasmic membrane in micro-organisms. Possibly the situation varies with the physiological state of the cells, but variation in the techniques employed by different investigators may account for some of the discrepancies observed (Rothstein, 1959).

Epstein (1955) estimated that the "outer space" of excised barley roots for a variety of salts is about 23 per cent of the tissue volume. The measurement was unaffected by external concentration of solute, pH, or by the presence of other ions in the medium. The space penetrated presumably includes a thin layer of water adhering to the root surface, and any water-filled spaces in and around the cell walls. Its value depends very much on the extent to which the intercellular spaces of the material are impregnated with water when the determinations are made.

If the freely accessible space within a cell or tissue contains immobile electrical charges or adsorption sites, the *actual* volume of tissue penetrated by salt may be different from that calculated by the method just described, because the concentration of ions in the space will be different from that in the external medium. For example, if Donnan equilibria are established in a space containing immobile anions the concentration of mobile cations will be higher, and that of mobile anions lower than in the medium, resulting in the first case in an over-estimation, and in the latter, an underestimation of the actual volume penetrated. For this reason it is often necessary to refer to the "apparent" free space (AFS) rather than the actual free space of a tissue or cell (Briggs and Robertson, 1957). AFS is therefore defined as the apparent volume of a cell or tissue penetrated passively by salt *assuming* that salt reaches the same concentration there as in the medium. From measurements of passive salt uptake from salt solutions of different concentration, it is possible to deduce that the apparent free space consists of two components, the WFS and a "Donnan-free space" (DFS) containing immobile anions. The lower the external concentration of salt, the greater the relative concentration of cations in the Donnan-free space and the greater the value of the apparent free space for cations. Conversely, the lower the external concentration, the lower the relative concentration of anions and the lower the calculated value of AFS for anions. Hope (1953) demonstrated that experimentally-determined values of AFS for chloride in bean (*Vicia faba*) roots placed in solutions of potassium chloride, increased with increasing external concentration in a manner consistent with the establishment of Donnan equilibria (Fig. 34b). It is sometimes possible to make a reasonable estimate of the *actual* volume occupied by free space, e.g. by microscopic observations assuming that penetration into the cytoplasm occurs; the concentration of immobile anions can then be calculated. By assuming that the Donnan-free space represents free space in the cytoplasm occupying 14 per cent of the tissue volume, Hope calculated that the average concentration of immobile anions in the

Donnan-free space of maize roots is about 10 m eq/l. In this calculation, the possibility that a fraction of the immobile anions were already associated with cations (e.g. calcium ions) when the tissue was placed in salt was neglected, and this may have led to an underestimation of the concentration of immobile anions in the Donnan-free space. More recent experiments with salt-saturated red beet tissue in which this source of error was minimised have yielded values of about 560 m eq/l. (Briggs *et al.* 1958).

Although the reality of a Donnan-free space has been established, its precise location remains a subject of debate. Levitt (1957) has argued convincingly that it can be adequately accommodated in cell wall spaces. Dainty and Hope (1959) have compared the reversible physical component of uptake in intact *Chara* plants with that in separated cellulose walls of the same organism, and have concluded likewise that the bulk of the Donnan-free space is located in the wall. According to this view the plasmalemma is an effective barrier to passive penetration and active mechanisms must be involved in the movement of ions across it. Arisz (1953) has supplied evidence that chloride absorption into the cytoplasm of *Vallisneria* leaf cells is more sensitive to inhibition by cyanide, and less sensitive to dinitrophenol poisoning than is the transfer of the ions into vacuoles. Both processes apparently depend on respiration.

Others (e.g. Robertson, 1951; Hope and Stevens, 1952, Butler, 1953) have suggested that the apparent free space may include at least a part of the cytoplasm. Possibly the truth lies between these two views, for the plasmalemma sometimes behaves as a cation-permeable/anion-impermeable membrane, across which anions are actively transported but cations exchange freely. Two facts make it exceedingly difficult to reach a definite conclusion regarding location of the DFS exclusively in the cell wall or partly in the cytoplasm.

   (i) There may be no sharp line of demarcation between the two, especially in young cells with actively growing walls which seem to originate from the bulk of the cytoplasm, and

   (ii) the outer surface of the cytoplasm may be extensively convoluted, enclosing within the cell an appreciable space which is in direct communication with the external medium. Electrical charges on the membrane would cause fine invaginations to behave as Donnan-free spaces.

A distinguishing feature of ions held in the free spaces of cells is that they will exchange readily with salt from the external medium. About 10 per cent of the potassium in excised barley roots and in storage tissue slices is rapidly exchangeable (Broyer and Overstreet, 1940; Sutcliffe, 1954b), the remainder exchanges more slowly, and is said to be located in the "non-free space" (NFS) which includes vacuoles and probably at least a part of the cytoplasm. MacRobbie and Dainty (1958a) distinguished three distinct phases in the cellular alga, *Nitellopsis obtusa*, on the basis of ion-exchange-ability:

(i) a free space including cellulose wall and perhaps part of the cytoplasm,

(ii) a so-called protoplasmic non-free space, and

(iii) a vacuolar non-free space.

From measurements of the changes in radioactivity of an external solution to which the plants were transferred after they had been immersed in solutions containing radioactive isotopes, it was possible to calculate the rates of movement of ions in both directions across the membranes separating these phases under defined conditions ("steady state fluxes"). The results are presented in Fig. 35a, together with values obtained for the potassium, sodium and chloride concentrations in the sap. The ratio of sodium to potassium ions in the protoplasmic non-free space was found to be the same as in the vacuole and to be higher there than in the external medium. MacRobbie and Dainty concluded that accumulation of these ions in the sap might occur passively along an electrochemical gradient created by active transport of chloride ions, although the relative impermeability of the inner membrane to cations seems to make this unlikely. The higher ratio of potassium to sodium in the sap and protoplasm was attributed to active excretion of sodium from protoplasm into the medium. More probably the protoplasm contains small vacuoles and vesicles which hold the bulk of the cations present in the protoplasmic non-free space, and which, like the sap, accumulate potassium in preference to sodium (see below). The concentration of chloride in the protoplasmic non-free space is apparently lower than in either the medium or the sap, leading MacRobbie and Dainty to suggest that this ion is actively transported from the protoplasm into the sap. Whether or not active processes

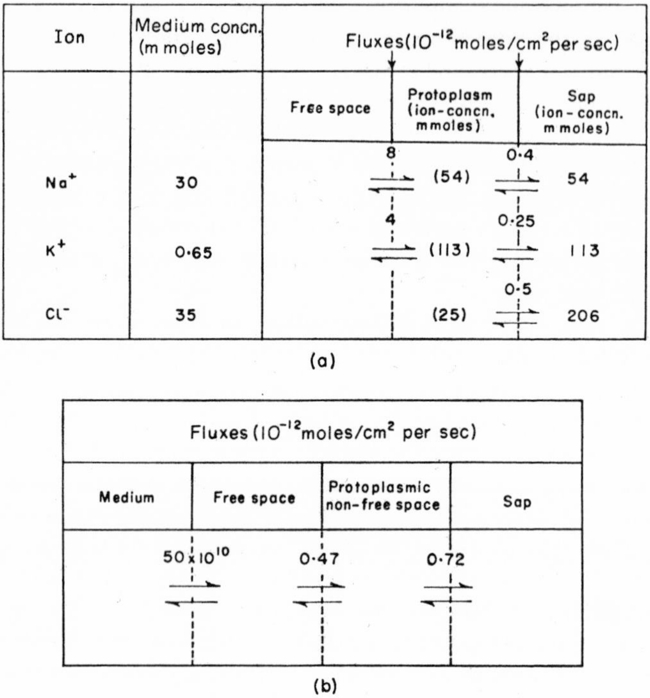

(a)

(b)

FIG. 35. Measurements of ion fluxes in algal cells.
a. Concentrations of ions in the sap of *Nitellopsis*, and estimated values of the fluxes between the different kinetic compartments within the cell. Only the ratio of the concentrations of the 3 ions in the protoplasmic non-free space was measured and the concentrations given in brackets are estimated values (redrawn from MacRobbie and Dainty, 1958a); b. Steady-state flux rates of exchange of potassium ions between different phases of *Nitella axillaris* cells (Diamond and Solomon, 1959).

are also involved in movement of chloride into the non-free space from the medium remains uncertain.

Diamond and Solomon (1959) distinguished three fractions with differing exchangeability in the potassium content of *Nitella axillaris*. The smallest fraction, containing about 0·1 per cent of the total potassium, exchanges most rapidly (apparent half time of exchange = 23 sec), and is probably located in the cell wall. The second fraction, comprising about 1·6 per cent of the total, exchanges more slowly (apparent half time = 5 hr) and may represent an intra-cytoplasmic component. The bulk of the salt in the algal cell occurs in the third fraction which exchanges very slowly (apparent half time = 40 days) and is probably contained in the central vacuole. Both the outer and inner protoplasmic membranes seem to be rather impermeable in this organism (see Fig. 35a).

Briggs and Pitman (1959) reported that the non-free space in red beet cells can similarly be separated into two components, a smaller fraction in which 50 per cent, of the ions exchange in 1 hr and a larger fraction with an apparent half time of exchange of about 1000 hr.

A somewhat puzzling observation, in view of the results just described, is the ready exchangeability of the bulk of the salt, in fronds of some sea-weeds. Scott *et al.* (1957), for example, observed that nearly 90 per cent of the sodium in *Ulva lactuca* fronds exchanges with sodium ions from the medium within 5 sec. The speed of this exchange is difficult to reconcile with accumulation of ions in vacuoles assuming that the cytoplasm has a similar permeability in all plant cells, and it seems likely that most of the sodium in this tissue is associated with extracellular mucilage and cell walls. Potassium ions exchange less rapidly than sodium ions in *Ulva lactuca*, but more readily than the bulk of potassium in higher plant cells and in coenocytes. They are lost quickly from *Ulva* fronds in darkness and reabsorbed upon illumination (Fig. 15b, p. 49). In contrast, salts accumulated in the vacuoles of higher plant cells are retained by the cytoplasm, even under conditions of reduced metabolism. It is possible that a large fraction of the potassium content of *Ulva* exists in the mucilaginous cell wall and in meta-bolically-bound forms in the cytoplasm, while relatively little is accumulated in vacuoles, which in any case are inextensive in this plant. The situation may thus be comparable to that found in bacteria and other micro-organisms (see pp. 97-8). MacRobbie and Dainty (1958b) distinguished rapidly and more slowly exchanging components in the salt content of the red alga, *Rhodymenia palmata*. Interpretation of their results in terms of the location of each component is difficult because of the structural complexity of this plant.

More investigations of the salt relations of relatively non-vacuolated cells might do much to clarify the mechanisms of ion absorption and retention in cytoplasm. Apart from micro-organisms, suitable experimental materials might be: meristematic cells in tissue culture, myxomycetes in the plasmodial condition, and leaves of certain mosses e.g. *Mnium punctatum*.

3. *Salt Relations of Cell Components*

a. Cell walls. Most plant cells are surrounded by a rigid wall containing cellulose, hemicelluloses, polyuronides (e.g. pectic acid, pectinic acid and pectin), lipids and protein. The water content of cell walls may be as high as 90 per cent or more (Frey-Wyssling, 1952) and most of them are freely permeable to salts in aqueous solution. The low resistance offered to diffusion of salts and other dissolved substances is demonstrated by the phenomenon of plasmolysis. Bennet-Clark and Bexon (1946) showed that when plasmolysed onion epidermis cells are transferred from one plasmolysing solution to another, the liquid in the intramural space rapidly equilibrates with the new medium. In mature cells, walls often become impregnated with fats and lignin (suberin) and are then much less permeable.

Cellulose, hemicelluloses, polyuronides and phospholipids are capable of binding salts in readily exchangeable forms, and the wall therefore behaves as a Donnan system containing an appreciable concentration of negative charges. Ions move through this system from the external medium, by diffusion and exchange, to the surface of the cytoplasm, and by virtue of its binding properties the wall exerts some effect on the availabilities of ions at this point. Readily available cations are held at a high concentration near the cytoplasmic surface, while the concentration of anions tends to be lower than in the external medium.

b. Cytoplasm. Early cytologists concluded that a distinct membrane exists within the cell wall at the outer surface of the cytoplasm and to this the terms "plasmalemma", "ectoplast" and "plasma membrane" have been applied. (Plate I, facing p. 95). Similarly, the cytoplasm is thought to be bounded on its inner surface by the "tonoplast" or "vacuolar membrane". Owing to the impermeability of these membranes, dyes injected into the cytoplasm are retained there. The mechanical stability of both the plasmalemma and tonoplast has, in some cases, been demonstrated by microdissection. Both membranes have about the same thickness (60–100 Å), and are composed principally of lipids and protein which are probably arranged somewhat as in Fig 36. The comparative ease with which vacuoles enclosed by the tonoplast can be separated from the remainder of the cytoplasm (see p. 21) suggests that there may be only a tenuous structural connection between them. It is across the tonoplast and plasmalemma that active transport is usually presumed to occur, but to look upon cytoplasm as a homogenous phase separated from sap and medium by bounding membranes which regulate its ion content is now seen to be a much too naive approach.

Within the surface membrane, cytoplasm consists of a complex aggregation of membranes, vesicles, and granules, the ultrastructure of which has as yet been incompletely elucidated (Plate I). There is

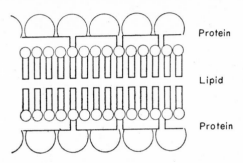

Protein

Lipid

Protein

FIG. 36. Diagrammatic representation of the arrangement of lipid and protein in a simple biological membrane (redrawn from Davson and Danielli, 1943).

apparently a continuous membrane system, the "endoplasmic reticulum", which divides the cytoplasm into two distinct phases, one of which is continuous with the nucleus, and the other perhaps with the external medium. The internal membranes are similar in structure to the surface membranes, and may in fact originate by growth and invagination of the plasmalemma (Buvat 1958). The relationship between endoplasmic reticulum and the tonoplast is likewise still not certain, but the impression given by electron micrographs is that the tonoplast is an independent structure not connected with intracellular membranes. If it is true that the plasmalemma is deeply invaginated and continuous with the endoplasmic reticulum, it is evident that the cytoplasm presents a much greater surface area to the external medium than has been thought. Ions which become bound from the medium on this membrane may be carried about by membrane flow as was suggested by Bennett (1956) and transported into the bulk of the cytoplasm by vesiculation (Fig. 12e, p. 43). Ions are thought to enter animal cells by a similar mechanism (Holter 1959). Evidence for invagination of the surface membrane in plants comes from electron microscopy of meristematic cells (Buvat, 1958; Whaley *et al.* 1960), and it is not possible at present to judge the situation in vacuolated parenchyma. During cell expansion, the cytoplasm is probably stretched as vacuolar volume increases, and invaginations of the surface membrane may tend to disappear in the mature turgid cell. This might account to some extent for the reduced rate of absorption of salts in turgid tissues (p. 63).

   c. Mitochondria. Mitochondria, chloroplasts, nuclei and vacuoles presumably compete with one another for salts transferred into the cytoplasm across the plasmalemma. Direct evidence that cytoplasmic particles accumulate salt was obtained by Mullins (1940). He allowed *Nitella* plants to absorb salt containing ^{42}K for a short time, and then centrifuged them so that the particles were moved to one end of each plant. It was found that the half of each cell which was richer in particles also showed the greater radioactivity. The particles in question were probably those which we now call mitochondria. These are easily recognizable cytoplasmic organelles, about $0·5\mu$ in diameter, 10μ or more in length (Plate I). Each mitochondrion is bounded by two parallel membranes, each 40–60Å thick, separated by a distance of 60–90Å. The inner membrane is invaginated to give rise to a system of internal membranes, the "cristae mitochondriales". Biochemically, mitochondria are recognized to be the sites of a number of important enzymes, including those involved in the Krebs cycle, and in oxidative phosphorylation.

   Considerable advances in knowledge of biochemistry have followed the discovery that mitochondria extracted from cells, with suitable precautions remain metabolically active. One of the necessary requirements is that the particles should be suspended in a medium of high osmotic pressure. If the osmotic pressure of the extracting medium is too low the mitochondria swell and burst. This is taken as evidence that the mitochondrial membranes are differentially permeable to water and solutes. The observation that mitochondria tend to congregate at secretory surfaces in animal tissues led Stanbury and Mudge (1953) and Bartley and Davies (1954) to examine the ability of isolated mitochondria to accumulate solutes. They found that actively metabolizing liver and kidney mitochondria are able to maintain concentration gradients for both inorganic ions and organic substances. Robertson *et al.* (1955) demonstrated that an ability to accumulate salt in mitochondria from red beet and carrot roots is correlated with metabolic activity. They concluded that whereas the accumulation of cations might be attributed at least partly to establishment of Donnan equilibria, accumulation of anions is probably due to active transport.

Robertson (1951) suggested that the primary act of salt accumulation occurs across the mitochondrial membranes, and in fact this is the only place at which the Lundegårdh mechanism could operate because all the cytochrome in non-green cells is located in mitochondria. The idea is supported by the capacity of isolated mitochondria to accumulate ions. It presupposes that the plasmalemma is permeable to ions so that salts can move freely from the medium into the cytoplasm. As already indicated it now seems unlikely that this is the case. Salts accumulated by the mitochondria might, according to Robertson, be transferred into vacuoles subsequently by disintegration of the particles at the tonoplast. There is no direct evidence to support this view and it seems more likely that mitochondria and vacuoles are independent accumulators of salts. If ions are accumulated in cytoplasmic organelles prior to transference into the central vacuole, these are more probably small vacuoles or vesicles with which the cytoplasm abounds (Plate I). The large central vacuole arises by coalescence of smaller vacuoles during development, and it is not impossible that this process continues even in mature cells. The energy for salt accumulation in vacuoles is presumably derived from high energy phosphorus compounds produced in mitochondria, as is the energy for other endergonic processes such as protein synthesis. Ions accumulated by mitochondria themselves are presumably retained and assist in maintenance of the turgidity and structural integrity of the organelle (cf. the function of salts in vacuoles).

d. Chloroplasts. Chloroplasts consist of densely packed lipoprotein lamellae and in comparison with mitochondria, their water content is relatively low so that a relatively large proportion of the salt they contain is likely to be bound to structural components.

Chloroplasts are surrounded by a distinct membrane, and because they swell in media of low osmotic pressure, it has been inferred that they behave as osmometers. The evidence that the surface membrane is selectively permeable is as yet inconclusive. Diamond and Solomon (1959) have demonstrated that the chloroplasts in *Nitella* cells do not represent a separate phase in the photoplasm as far as the exchangeability of potassium ions is concerned.

Gross analyses of isolated chloroplasts indicate that their salt content is often not strikingly different from that of the cell as a whole. Alkali and alkali earth cations are somewhat less abundant in chloroplasts than in mitochondria or vacuoles, and this may be related to the fact that they exist mainly as free ions in aqueous solution. On the other hand, ions such as phosphate, iron and zinc which become readily incorporated into organic complexes tend to be more abundant in chloroplasts than elsewhere. Arnon (1955) has shown that in addition to being capable of photolysis of water and reduction of carbon dioxide, isolated chloroplasts in the light incorporate inorganic phosphate into organic phosphorus compounds ("photophosphorylation"). It would be interesting to examine the possibility that photophosphorylation can promote absorption of other ions than phosphate into chloroplasts and intact cells.

B. Transport from Cell to Cell

The protoplasm in a multicellular organism is continuous from one cell to another via protoplasmic connections ("plasmadesmata") (Fig. 5g, p. 19), forming a "symplast", and it is apparently through these that ions are transported from cell to cell. It is probable that some salt is carried bound to the membranes of the endoplasmic reticulum which are continuous between cells, and in constant movement (cf. pp. 105-6). The large central vacuoles are not continuous from cell to cell, and are unlikely to have a direct influence on movement of salts. Small vacuoles, however, may move through the protoplasmic connections and could act as vehicles in salt transport.

Movement of ions through parenchyma has been studied in leaves of a water plant, *Vallisneria spiralis* by Arisz, and his associates in the Netherlands (Arisz, 1953; Arisz and Schreuder, 1956; Arisz and Sol, 1956). It was found that when excised leaf segments are placed on the surface of agar containing sodium or potassium chloride, chloride is absorbed. If salt is supplied in this way to only part of the leaf segment (absorption zone) transport to other regions can be examined. It was observed that when the absorption zone is illuminated, chloride tends to accumulate in that area, and little is transferred elsewhere especially when the rest of the leaf is kept in

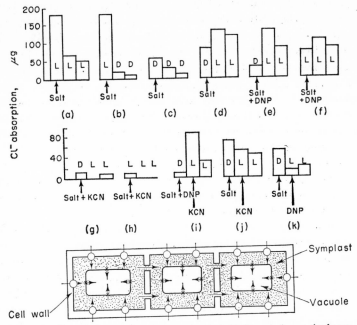

FIG. 37. Absorption and transport of *chloride* in *Vallisneria* leaves (redrawn from Arisz, 1953). a-k ⊙ Effects of light and metabolic inhibitors on accumulation of chloride in different zones of leaf segments L=zone exposed to light; D=zone exposed to darkness; KCN=potassium cyanide $(3 \times 10^{-4}M)$; DNP=dinitrophenol $(10^{-4}M)$; Lower diagram summarises the interpretation of a-k-%%location of an absorption mechanism sensitive to cyanide × location of a mechanism sensitive to dinitrophenol, and stimulated by light.

darkness (Fig. 37abc). Darkening the absorption zone when the rest of the leaf was illuminated reduces accumulation in that region and promotes transport elsewhere (Fig. 37d). These results were explained on the assumptions that absorption of salt by a vacuolated cell is a two-stage process involving, firstly, entry into cytoplasm and secondly transference into the vacuole, and that cell to cell transfer occurs through the cytoplasm (Fig. 37). Illuminated cells tend to accumulate salt in vacuoles, and therefore little is available for transport elsewhere when the absorption zone is exposed to light. Illumination of cells in the receptor zones, likewise stimulates vacuolar accumulation, and promotes transport of salts towards them from the absorption zone.

Evidence that movement from zone to zone occurs via cytoplasm rather than by diffusion through cell walls was obtained by experiments with metabolic inhibitors. Accumulation of chloride in all parts of the leaf was prevented when potassium cyanide (3×10^{-4}M) was applied to the absorption zone (Fig. 37g, h). This would not be expected if salt moved passively through cell walls, unless, indeed, the inhibitor also travelled along a similar path in sufficient amounts to prevent absorption in the recipient zones. That the latter is not the case was shown by the failure of potassium cyanide to inhibit uptake by the absorption zone when it was supplied elsewhere (Fig. 37j). Cyanide at this concentration evidently inhibits uptake of chloride into the protoplasm of *Vallisneria* cells, but does not interfere with accumulation in vacuoles or with transport through the symplast.

Dinitrophenol (10^{-4}M) was found to inhibit accumulation in the zone to which it was applied, presumably through an effect on transport into vacuoles (Fig. 37 e, f, i, k). When supplied to the absorption zone (Fig. 39 e, f, i) it did not apparently interfere with transport and accumulation of salt elsewhere, but in the case (Fig. 37 k) where it was applied to a recipient zone, there is some indication that it prevented transport across that region into a terminal zone. In more recent work (Arisz, 1958) it has been demonstrated that a number of other metabolic inhibitors, which affect either vacuolar accumulation (e.g. azide) or uptake into cytoplasm (arsenate and uranyl ions) do not influence transport from zone to zone, and this seems to support the somewhat surprising conclusion that movement of salts in cytoplasm is mainly a passive process. More experiments with *Vallisneria* leaves and other materials are required before such a conclusion can be fully justified.

For further reading

ARISZ, W. H. (1953). Active uptake, vacuole-secretion and plasmatic transport of chloride ions in leaves of *Vallisneria spiralis*. *Acta Bot. Néerl.* **1**, 506–15.
BRIGGS, G. E. and ROBERTSON, R. N. (1957). Apparent free space. *Ann. Rev. Plant Physiol.* **8**, 11–29.

CHAPTER 7

SALT RELATIONS OF VASCULAR PLANTS

I am indeed not unaware that this path is obscured by clouds which will pass over from time to time. Yet these clouds will easily be dispersed when it is possible to make the fullest use of the light of experience. For Nature always resembles herself although she often seems to us, on account of the inevitable deficiency of our observations, to disagree with herself.

C. LINNAEUS.

A.   ZONES OF ION ABSORPTION IN ROOTS

WHEN excised or attached roots are placed for a short time in a solution of salts containing a radioactive ion, it is often observed that a zone near the tip becomes more radioactive than do more mature regions (Fig. 38a). Radioactivity is not, however, confined to the extreme root apex, and whereas a region of low activity frequently coincides with the zone of cell elongation, there is often a region of high radioactivity in the root hair zone (Fig. 38b). Such experiments indicate that different regions of the root retain salts to differing extents, but do not, as has sometimes been thought, provide much information as to the most active zone of absorption. The low concentration of absorbed salt in the zone of elongation, for example, could be attributed to concomitant growth by uptake of water, or to transport of salts away from this region rather than to a slow rate of absorption. Wiebe and Kramer (1954) attributed the accumulation of salts near the tip of roots to the high metabolic activity in this region, and to the absence of conducting tissue (see Fig. 3a, p. 15). They demonstrated that only a small percentage of various ions absorbed by the terminal 4 mm of barley roots is translocated elsewhere (Table 8) whereas as much as 34 per cent of the phosphate taken up was transported away from one of the more mature zones. When salt is supplied to the extreme tip of *Vicia faba* roots, Brouwer (1954) found in agreement with Wiebe and Kramer, that little or no transport to the more basal zones occurs. On the contrary, even though the root apex absorbs ions directly from the medium, it normally obtains some of its salt supply from more basal regions. Brouwer demonstrated that the relative amounts of salt taken up at different points along the bean root, varies with the rate of concomitant water absorption. When water absorption by the plant was increased, uptake of salt by the extreme tip was unchanged, but that by the more mature zones increased. Some possible explanations of this observation will be given below.

TABLE 8. TRANSLOCATION OF SALTS FROM DIFFERENT REGIONS OF THE BARLEY ROOT.   (Data of Wiebe and Kramer, 1954).

Distance from root tip at which isotope was supplied (mm)	Percentage of absorbed isotope translocated elsewhere			
	^{32}P	^{86}Rb	^{131}I	^{35}S
0– 4	1·3	4·2	1·0	1·7
7–10	8·5	14·3	28·3	5·2
27–30	34·4	14·7	28·9	11·8
57–60	24·9	9·4	22·7	9·2

B. SALT ABSORPTION AND TRANSPIRATION

If the movement of salts into roots occurs partly or entirely by mass flow, as early botanists suggested, it should be possible to demonstrate a relationship between the rates of absorption of salts and water. Many experiments have been performed to examine the situation, and the results show that in some cases the two processes are entirely independent, while, in others, salt absorption increases with increased transpiration, to a greater or lesser extent.

Van den Honert (1933) studied phosphate and water absorption by sugar cane plants growing in well aerated salt solutions. He observed that during the hours of daylight, transpiration was about ten times greater than at night but phosphate absorption was little affected (Fig. 39a; see also Fig. 39b). Such variation in salt absorption as occurred was attributed to fluctuations in temperature.

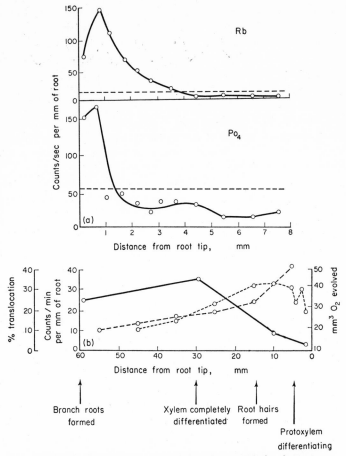

FIG. 38. Zones of salt absorption and accumulation in roots
a. Radioactivity of various regions of living barley roots after immersion in rubidium phosphate containing ^{86}Rb and ^{32}P, for 3 hr at 25 °C. The dotted line indicated radioactivity in a comparable volume of medium. (Redrawn from Overstreet and Jacobson, 1946); b. Respiration rate ($\bigcirc$---$\bigcirc$), accumulation of ^{32}P ($\bigcirc$— — —$\bigcirc$), and translocation of ^{32}P ($\bigcirc$—$\bigcirc$) in different zones of barley roots (redrawn from Kramer, 1956).

In more recent experiments using a similar technique, Van den Honert *et al.* (1955) observed no significant effects of transpiration rate on absorption of ammonium, potassium, nitrate and phosphate ions by *Zea mays*. Broyer and Hoagland (1943) showed that

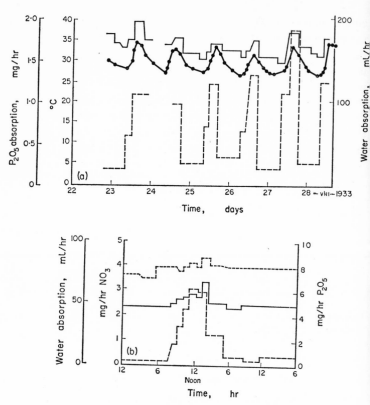

FIG. 39. Transpiration and salt absorption

a. Rates of water (— — —) and phosphate absorption (●—●) by a sugar cane plant during several days. Root temperature indicated thus (—) (redrawn from Van den Honert, 1933); b. Rates of water (— — —) phosphate (—) and nitrate (---) absorption by a plant of *Sanchezia nobilis* during 36 hr (redrawn from Van den Honert, Hooymans and Volkers, 1955).

absorption of salts in intact barley and *Cucurbita* plants was more markedly affected by factors which influence respiration, for example aeration and temperature, than by those affecting water absorption, such as illumination and humidity. Plants which were initially low in salts absorbed about the same amounts of potassium and bromide ions in light and darkness, and at high and low humidity, although the amounts of water absorbed under the different conditions varied greatly (Table 9). Moreover, about an equal amount of salt was transferred into the shoots under the various conditions, thus disposing of the objection that uptake by these plants was mainly due to accumulation in the roots. Some increase of salt absorption at high transpiration rates was obtained with plants which had a high initial salt content. The stimulation resulting from illumination was attributed to promotion of photosynthesis rather than to increased transpiration, on the assumption that sugar content limits uptake in high salt plants which are characteristically low in carbohydrates. In addition, the high

TABLE 9. INFLUENCE OF TRANSPIRATION ON ABSORPTION AND TRANSLOCATION OF SALTS BY BARLEY PLANTS.
(Data of Broyer and Hoagland 1943).

Plants	Environmental conditions	Water absorbed (ml/gf wt. of shoot)	Salt absorbed (m eq. $\times 10^2/$ g f.wt. of plant)		Calculated Br conc. in xylem sap (m eq./l.)
			K+	Br⁻	
Low-salt status	Low humidity light	9·60	10·85	9·52	9·7
	High humidity light	3·60	10·40	9·65	25·1
	High humidity dark	2·52	8·75	9·13	27·8
High-salt status	Low humidity light	8·10	5·20	6·07	6·7
	High humidity light	2·58	3·24	4·24	14·8
	High humidity dark	1·49	1·39	2·15	9·8

concentration of salt in the xylem sap of high-salt plants, may serve to depress further absorption of ions at low transpiration rates (see below).

A number of other investigators have observed stimulation of salt absorption with increasing transpiration rates, but in most cases the two changes are by no means proportionate, and different ions are frequently affected differently (Table 10). Schmidt (1936) claimed that a linear relationship exists between water absorption and that of various ions in young plants of *Sanchezia nobilis*. Regression lines plotted from his results, except those for nitrate, seem to pass through the origin indicating that salt absorption stops at zero water absorption. No other investigator has reported such complete dependence of salt uptake on concomitant absorption of water.

Hylmö (1953, 1955, 1958) observed a large effect of transpiration on the absorption of calcium and chloride ions by 3-week old pea plants, and concluded that a major part of the salt transported into the shoot is carried across the root cortex in the transpiration stream by mass flow. A part of the salt taken into the plants in these experiments was retained by the roots, and of this a small fraction was absorbed independently of water absorption, while the remainder increased in amount as the rate of transpiration was increased.

TABLE 10. ABSORPTION OF WATER (ML) AND UPTAKE OF VARIOUS IONS (M EQ.)
BY PLANTS OF *Phaseolus vulgaris* IN 96 HR.
(Wright, 1939).

Treatment	Plant group	Phosphate	Calcium	Nitrate	Potassium	Water absorbed
Low humidity	A	13·6	25·0	41·4	35·6	330
High humidity	B	8·6	15·0	41·0	27·8	150
Low humidity	B	11·2	27·0	46·8	56·4	325
High humidity	A	9·6	13·0	41·8	52·8	165

This last observation was taken to indicate that inner cells of the root cortex receive a part of their salt supply via the transpiration stream, and absorb salt less quickly when this supply is reduced (see below). Brouwer (1954, 1956) concluded, in contrast to Hylmö, that passive influx of salt in the transpiration stream plays a minor role in rye, *Zea mays* and *Vicia faba*, because he found that dinitrophenol (10^{-5} M) inhibits chloride absorption without a comparable effect on water absorption, whereas increasing the osmotic pressure of the external medium interferes with water absorption, but not with that of salt. Such effects of transpiration on salt absorption as Brouwer observed were attributed to the influence of water stress on the "conductivity" of the root cortex, that is on the resistance presented to metabolic transport.

The relative importance of passive and active components in the absorption of salts by plants probably varies between species, and particularly with the conditions under which they are grown. High transpiration rates clearly cause an enhancement of the passive component whereas factors favouring rapid metabolism, e.g. aeration and moderately high temperatures favour active absorption. Mass flow is relatively less important at low external salt concentrations, because it varies linearly with concentration, whereas active absorption usually does not (see Chapter 4, pp. 55-7). Damaged roots absorb salts passively to a greater extent than intact ones, and mature roots may also be expected to present less resistance to passive movements of salts, than do young actively growing root systems. The predominating influence of metabolic mechanisms of absorption in young plants under normal conditions is indicated by the existence of root pressure, and by the preferential transference of certain ions from roots into shoots (see below).

Although the evidence shows that there are effects of transpiration rate on salt absorption, at least under some conditions, this does not necessarily mean that transpiration served a useful function in mineral nutrition. There is no evidence that when the rate of transpiration is low, plants suffer from salt deficiency. Hoagland (1944) showed that barley plants grown for several weeks with salt supplied only during the night when transpiration was low, contained as much salt at the end of the growing period as did other plants which received salts during the hours of daylight when transpiration was much higher. Species which naturally have a low transpiration rate, tend to grow and absorb salts more slowly than do species which are characterized by rapid transpiration, but it is not likely that the different rates of growth are due to differences in salt supply induced by the level of transpiration. The complex interrelationships of growth, transpiration, salt absorption, photosynthesis and other metabolic processes cannot be disentangled at present.

C. Transport across the Root Cortex

Ions entering the root surface move predominantly in a transverse direction across the cortex towards the stele (see Fig. 3, p. 15). Those which are not retained by intervening cells are transferred mainly into the xylem, and from there are carried into the shoot. A small fraction moves into the phloem and travels to the root apex (cf. p. 112).

The passive component of salt probably travels principally in the transpiration stream through wet cell walls in the more mature regions of the root, via "passage" cells in the endodermis, where the Casparian band (p. 15) is absent or incomplete, and directly into the cavities of the conducting elements. The possibility that salts and water traverse the cortex passively through the cytoplasm has also been suggested (Kramer, 1957). If cytoplasm forms part of the free space of a tissue, it may represent a significant channel for passive ion movement, but present opinion is against such an idea (see Chapter 6, p. 100).

There are two possible routes along which salts are transported actively into the stele. In the first, ions may be taken up into the cytoplasm of the surface cells of the root, transported from cell to cell via the plasmadesmata, and released from the cytoplasm adjoining the conducting elements into the xylem sap. In the second, they may move passively in cell walls as far as the endodermis and be transported actively from this point via cytoplasm into the stele. The relative importance of the two pathways is not certain. Measurements of the apparent free space of roots (Hope and Stevens, 1952; Butler, 1953; Epstein, 1955) indicate that a considerable volume of the root (10–35 per cent) is passively penetrated by salt. This probably means that the surface layer of cells does not present an impermeable barrier to diffusion and mass flow, and that ions can move relatively freely in the walls of the cortex cells, as far as the endodermis, where further penetration is probably retarded by the lipid-impregnated Casparian band. That the root surface does, however, present some resistance to passive movement of salts is indicated by an observation of Sandström (1950) that when an outer layer of cells is removed by immersing roots for a short time in di-n-amylacetic acid, absorption of salt subsequently occurs at an increased rate.

The amount of salt which penetrates passively through cell walls as far as the endodermis probably depends on the absorptive activity of cells located nearer the surface, and on the concentration of salts in the medium. When the external concentration of salt is low, it is possible that most of the salt has been extracted from the transpiration stream before it reaches the boundary of the stele. Ions absorbed into the cytoplasm of cortex cells, either directly from the medium, or from the transpiration stream, are then either transferred into central vacuoles or transmitted via the plasmadesmata towards the xylem. Salts do not usually pass through the central vacuoles of cortical cells on their way into the stele. The vacuoles seem rather to compete for available salts in the cytoplasm, removing a part of that which would otherwise move into the xylem. Salts accumulated in cortical vacuoles are not however irretrievably sealed off from the rest of the plant, and under conditions of salt starvation they may subsequently be released again and transferred elsewhere (Steward *et al.* 1942). As may be expected, roots of intact plants which have a low salt content, retain a higher proportion of the salt absorbed by the plant, than do roots whose salt content is high (Broyer, 1950). It has been shown in barley plants that as the external concentration of phosphate is decreased, a smaller proportion of that which is absorbed reaches the shoot (Russell and Martin, 1953).

Various hypotheses have been proposed to account for the active transport of salts from the medium into the non-living xylem elements. Crafts and Broyer (1938) suggested that salts absorbed actively into the cytoplasm of surface cells, move passively through the symplast (see p. 108) along a concentration gradient. The cytoplasm of living cells in the stele adjoining the conducting elements is perhaps incapable of retaining salts to the same extent as can those situated near the root surface, because of the relatively anaerobic conditions existing in centre of the root, and salts are thus released. Somewhat similar suggestions have been made by Wiersum (1948) and by Lundegårdh (1954). There is no evidence for the postulated gradient, nor has it been possible to demonstrate that there is in fact a deficiency of oxygen in the stele of roots.

Another possibility is that ions are bound to cytoplasmic constituents or accumulated in submicroscopic vesicles, and actively transported by protoplasmic streaming through the symplast to an inner protoplasmic boundary across which they are released, either actively or passively. On the basis of this idea, a series of analogies can be drawn between the salt relations of a single vacuolated cell and the multicellular root (Table 11). In both systems, the mechanisms of movement of ions into the cytoplasm, through it, and out into either vacuole or xylem sap, are possibly the same. Elucidation of the processes involved in the simpler system represented by the parenchyma cells should lead rapidly to greater understanding of the situation in the root.

Analyses of xylem sap have shown that salts can be accumulated in the conducting elements against existing concentration gradients, in the same way as in vacuoles (Table 12). Efficient active accumulation in the stele necessitates the existence of a permeability barrier in the root corresponding to the tonoplast in a cell. This barrier may be located, as Priestley (1920) suggested, at the endodermis, where the presence of the Casparian bands prevents leakage of aqueous solutions inwards or outwards along radial and transverse walls. If this is the case, the endodermis may function as a secretory layer comparable to those encountered in animals (e.g. amphibian skin, and gut epithelium). After being actively transported across the endodermis, ions might leak passively through the walls of any

TABLE 11. POSSIBLE ANALOGIES BETWEEN PARTS OF A VACUOLATED CELL AND MULTI-CELLULAR ROOT.
(From: Sutcliffe, 1959).

Vacuolated cell	Root
Plasmalemma	Root surface
Cytoplasm	Symplast
Tonoplast	Protoplasmic surface adjoining non-living xylem elements.
Vacuole	Cavities of xylem elements
Vacuolar sap	Xylem sap
Mitochondria (as independent accumulation units)	Vacuoles of cortex cells

intervening cells into the cavities of the xylem elements. Alternatively, the secretory mechanism may be located at the surface of living cells adjoining the xylem vessels, and the closely packed cells of the stele may present a sufficient resistance to allow development of a concentration gradient between xylem sap and medium. This situation needs further investigation. The establishment of a concentration gradient between the xylem sap and external medium is responsible for movement of water by osmosis, across the root, leading to the development of root pressure. As may be expected, root pressure diminishes when salts are withheld from the medium, or when the roots are placed under conditions of reduced metabolism. The existence of root pressure testifies to the importance of active processes in the transport of salts into the stele.

Active transport of salt into the xylem sap has another feature in common with vacuolar accumulation, namely the selectivity exhibited between ions. Some ions, e.g. iron and manganese, tend to be more concentrated relative to other cations in roots than in shoots, and this is attributable to formation of insoluble inorganic salts (e.g. insoluble phosphates) or organic complexes, which render the ions unavailable for transfer into the shoot. In other cases, however,

TABLE 12. CONCENTRATIONS OF IONS IN THE XYLEM SAP OF INTACT PLANTS UNDER CONDITIONS OF HIGH AND LOW TRANSPIRATION AND AT VARIOUS EXTERNAL SALT CONCENTRATIONS.
(From: Russell and Shorrocks, 1959).

Ion	Concentration in medium (ppm)	Plant	Ratio of ion concentration in xylem sap to that of medium.	
			Transpiration	
			High	Low
Phosphate	0·1	Barley	12·0	156·0
	0·1	Barley	24·0	108·0
	0·1	Sunflower	34·0	145·0
	0·1	Sunflower	11·0	50·0
	31·0	Barley	1·1	3·3
	31·0	Barley	0·6	2·3
	31·0	Sunflower	0·6	1·4
	31·0	Sunflower	0·5	0·9
Rubidium	0·31	Barley	36·0	73·0
	0·28	Barley	20·0	32·0
	1·34	Sunflower	3·7	2·7
	85·0	Barley	2·3	8·4
	85·0	Barley	3·6	2·2
	85·0	Barley	1·8	2·6
	85·0	Barley	0·8	0·7
	85·0	Barley	1·1	0·7

the characteristic distribution of salts between shoots and roots depends on discrimination between ions in the transport of salt out of the root. Potassium ions, for example, move into the shoot, in preference to sodium ions which tend to be left behind to accumulate in the root. This effect is not due to selective absorption of sodium ions into vacuoles of the root cortex cells allowing an excess of potassium ions to move into the stele, at least in barley plants, because excised root systems also exhibit a preference for potassium over sodium when both ions are supplied in the external medium (Sutcliffe, 1957).

D.   UPWARD TRANSPORT OF SALTS

In the discussion so far it has been assumed that inorganic solutes transported, by whatever mechanism, into the stele, are carried upwards in the transpiration stream. Evidence supporting this contention may be summarized as follows:

(i). Tracheal sap has been analysed and shown to contain appreciable amounts of salt. Since the sap moves upwards, it is inevitable that salts are carried along with it into the shoot.

(ii). Ringing experiments have shown that when a section of bark is removed there is little or no direct interference with movement of solutes into the shoot. Removal of a section of xylem severely limits or entirely prevents longitudinal transport (Clements and Engard, 1938; Phillis and Mason, 1940).

(iii). An objection can be raised against ringing experiments that the tissues remaining may behave abnormally after the operation. However, with the aid of radioactive isotopes, the upward transport of mineral salts in xylem can be demonstrated without disturbing the longitudinal continuity of any tissue. Stout and Hoagland (1939) separated lengths of bark from the wood in willow and geranium plants by inserting pieces of parchment through longitudinal incisions in the bark. After feeding salts labelled with radioactive isotopes to the roots, radioactivity was detected soon afterwards in the wood of the treated region, but not in the phloem. In places where bark and wood remained in physical contact, rapid transfer of isotope from one tissue to the other occurred.

(iv). If longitudinal transport takes place in the transpiration stream, the rate at which salts are transferred from roots to leaves should be related to the intensity of transpiration. In fact, under conditions favouring rapid transpiration, salts move much more quickly through the stems of tomato plants, than when transpiration was low. On a bright sunny day, radioactivity was detected in the tip of a tomato plant over 6 ft tall, 40 min after labelled phosphate had been supplied to the roots (Arnon *et al.* 1940), whereas under less favourable conditions such movement may require several hours.

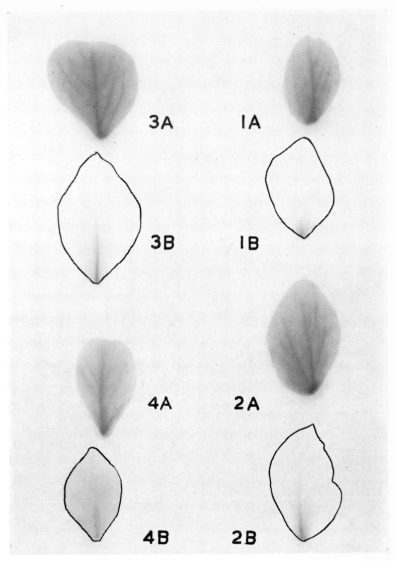

PLATE II. Transport of radioactive rubidium ions into bean leaves. The leaflets are numbered from the base of the stem upwards. Series B were covered with polythene bags to reduce transpiration, and series A left uncovered (Sutcliffe, unpublished).

(v). When transpiration is stopped in a particular leaf or leaflet, the amount of salt delivered to that structure is drastically curtailed, as was demonstrated in a simple experiment with *Vicia faba* plants (see Plate II facing p. 122).

Care must be taken to distinguish between the rate at which an individual ion is transported over a given distance, and the total quantity of salt moved in a given interval of time. The former depends on the linear rate of mass flow, and its measurement is affected by the sensitivity of technique employed. The more sensitive the method of detection, the more rapid the apparent rate of transport. The total quantity of salt transported on the other

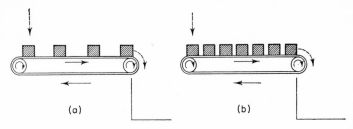

(a)   (b)

Fig. 40.   Diagram illustration transport of objects on a mechanical conveyor
a. Objects supplied at a rate of 1 per sec; endless belt moving at the rate of 1 ft/sec; delivery at the rate of 1 per sec; b. Object supplied at the same rate as in a; belt moving at the rate of 6 ins/sec; delivery is at the same rate as in a, but the belt becomes more heavily loaded.

hand, is a function of the rate of flow of the solution by volume, and the concentration of salt contained in it. Comparison with a mechanical conveyor will make the distinction clear (see Fig. 40). If a single article is placed on the machine, its rate of transport will depend on the rate of movement of the conveyor belt, but if a number of articles are supplied the rate of delivery will ultimately depend on the rate of supply, and will be independent within limits of the rate of movement of the belt. If the belt moves more slowly it will merely become more heavily loaded than when it moves quickly (Fig. 40b). It is only when the rate of movement of the belt is so slow that it is unable to accept articles at the rate supplied, or when it stops completely, that the speed of the conveyor controls the rate of delivery.

A similar situation arises in the transport of salt by mass flow in the xylem. Within rather wide limits, the rate at which salts are delivered to the leaves is determined by the rate at which they are supplied to the conducting elements in the roots. At slower rates of flow, the concentration of xylem sap is increased (Table 12, p. 121) so that the total quantity of salt transported remains approximately the same. One effect of an increasing concentration of salts in the xylem sap is to reduce transport into the stele from the cortex of the root (cf the effect of internal concentration on vacuolar accumulation, Chapter 4, pp. 65-6). In this way transpiration rate exerts an indirect influence on salt absorption into the root (see p. 115).

Anderssen (1929) found that the total concentration of electrolytes in xylem sap from the outer annual rings of pear and apricot trees is almost twice that in the inner rings. Since water is also transported most rapidly in young xylem, it is likely that in trees most of the mineral salts are carried through the most recently formed wood. The amounts of salt transported also vary with season. Bollard (1953) found that the amount of nitrogen, phosphorus, potassium and magnesium in the tracheal sap of apple trees in New Zealand is low during the winter. This is presumably the result of low rates of absorption of salts by the roots, since the movement of water is also slow. The concentration of the xylem sap increases rapidly during spring, reaching a maximum several weeks after flowering, and then gradually declines again until the low winter level is attained (Fig. 41).

In addition to inorganic salts, xylem sap contains a variety of organic substances, including nitrogenous and phosphorus compounds. Bollard (1957) demonstrated the presence of a variety of organic nitrogen compounds, including amino acids and amides in the xylem sap of a wide range of plants, and the possibility must be considered that an appreciable part of the nitrogen transported into the shoot is carried in organic forms produced in the roots following reduction of nitrate. Phosphoryl-choline and glyceryl phosphoryl-choline are among the substances detected in sap exuding from excised barley roots, and it has been claimed that about 20 per cent of the phosphorus transported in the xylem occurs in the form of these substances (Tolbert and Wiebe, 1955). Sulphur seems to move upwards in the stem entirely as the sulphate (Thomas *et al.* 1944), and there is no doubt that the bulk of the metallic cations are also transported as free ions.

E. DISTRIBUTION OF SALTS IN THE SHOOT

As the transpiration stream ascends the stem, ions are absorbed from it by the surrounding tissues, notably by the cambium, and the concentration of solutes is reduced. For this reason, leaves which are inserted higher on the plant receive through the xylem less salt for a given amount of water absorbed than do those located lower down. In spite of this, the salt content of the former tends to be greater than that of the latter; Biddulph (1951) demonstrated an approximately linear relationship between the logarithm of the con-

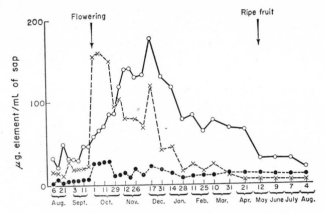

FIG. 41. Composition of xylem sap of an apple tree showing seasonal variation in New Zealand O——O = potassium x— — —x = nitrogen; ●----● = phosphorus (redrawn from Bollard, 1953).

centration of phosphate in leaves, and their position on the stem of *Phaseolus vulgaris* (Fig. 42). Young leaves evidently receive an additional supply of salts, and this comes from older leaves via the phloem. Steward (see Steward and Millar, 1954) has shown that leaves in the same orthostichy tend to function as a nutritional unit, and this is related to the presence of vascular connections between them. The bulk of the salt accumulating in storage organs, such as fruits and tubers, comes indirectly from the leaves via the phloem rather than directly in the transpiration stream. Export of mineral salts from mature leaves can easily be demonstrated with radio active tracers (see below), but even without such techniques it is readily observable just prior to leaf fall when the concentration of certain ions, notably potassium and phosphate in the leaves, falls rapidly.

Growing tissues compete with one another to a certain extent for the available salt supply. Arnon and Hoagland (1943) showed that if tomato plants are grown in a complete nutrient medium until the flowering stage, and then transferred to one lacking phosphate, some fruits are formed at the expense of phosphorus withdrawn from

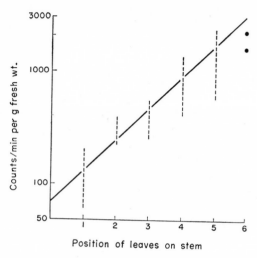

FIG. 42. Amounts of ^{32}P detected in various leaves on the stem of *Phaseolus vulgaris* plants after absorption of labelled phosphate for 4 days. Oldest leaf=1; youngest=6. The vertical lines indicate the spread of points obtained in numerous determinations (redrawn from Biddulph, 1951).

leaves and stems, but the yield is much reduced. Plants which were de-flowered after transfer to the phosphate-free medium made more vegetative growth, than did those which were allowed to fruit, and growth was at the expense of salt absorbed from older tissues. Williams (1948) found that when oat plants are grown under conditions of low phosphate supply, phosphorus required for development of the inflorescence is obtained mainly from the medium, but when plants have been grown in the presence of an abundant supply of phosphate, and thus have a high phosphorus content, a larger amount is supplied from stems and leaves (Fig. 43).

The ability of growing organs to accumulate salts at the expense of non-growing tissues is a well-established phenomenon, but the reason why nutrients are diverted in this way is far from understood. Presumably, in the growing tissue, salts are accumulated in vacuoles or utilized in the synthesis of cell constituents to such an extent that

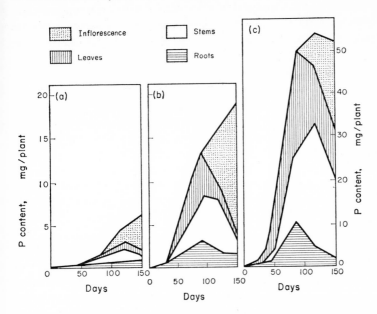

FIG. 43. The pattern of distribution and redistribution of phosphorus in oat plants with varying phosphorus supply. a. low phosphorus supply; b. medium phosphorus supply; c. high phosphorus supply (redrawn from Williams, 1948).

the concentration of free ions in the cytoplasm is reduced, and this stimulates salt movement towards the "sink" from the ends of the sieve tubes through the cytoplasm of surrounding cells. The mechanism may be fundamentally similar to that involved in the polarized movement of salt across the root cortex towards the stele (see pp. 117f).

Calcium ions are not transported in the phloem, and it is for this reason that the calcium content of leaves does not decrease before leaf fall, as is the case with other ions. The calcium content of many fruits is relatively low, because of a dependence on supply via a rather sluggish transpiration stream. In a few cases, e.g. the peanut (*Arachis hypogaea*) where transpiration is still further reduced because the fruits develop underground, some calcium and other salts are taken up directly from the soil via specialized absorptive structures, the gynaphores.

The idea that mineral salts circulate in plants, travelling upwards in the xylem and downwards in the phloem was suggested by Mason and Maskell (1931) in the course of their investigations of solute movement in the cotton plant. They proposed that phosphorus and potassium are sometimes transported downwards to the roots at a greater rate than they are utilized there, so that they re-enter the xylem, and are recirculated. In an attempt to demonstrate circulation of ions, Biddulph *et al.* (1958) supplied calcium, phosphate and sulphate labelled with radioactive isotopes to the roots of intact bean (*Phaseolus vulgaris*) plants for 1 hr, and then examined the subsequent migration of the radioactivity over a period of several days, while the plant was growing in an non-radioactive solution. Labelled phosphate was carried up the stem and into the leaves as a discrete unit. Later it moved into the roots again, and continued to circulate until the end of the experiment. Circulation of sulphate was rapidly curtailed by metabolic incorporation in young leaves, and calcium did not circulate at all.

Salts accumulated by storage tissues are redistributed during a subsequent phase of the life cycle. During the early stages in the development of seeds, for example, salt is supplied to the young radicle and plumule from the cotyledons. Biddulph (1951) observed a movement of iron from the cotyledons of germinating bean seeds (Fig. 44a) which closely parallels that of carbohydrates. Roots of seedlings grown under conditions of sulphur deficiency were found to receive higher proportions of the sulphur leaving the cotyledons than they did when sulphur was supplied in the medium. In pea plants, grown in potassium-deficient media in the dark, potassium was transferred from the cotyledons during the first 10 days, about equally into roots and shoots (Fig. 44b). Movement into roots became very slow after about 2 weeks, at a time when they also ceased to grow. When aeration of the roots was reduced, the amount of potassium absorbed, and of growth, decreased without affecting either the salt content or growth of the shoot. Removal of the shoot at an early stage leaving the cotyledons intact did not significantly alter root growth or influence the rate at which potassium was transported into them from the cotyledons.

F. FOLIAR ABSORPTION

Aquatic vascular plants, for example *Elodea, Lemna* and *Vallisneria* species, absorb the bulk of their nutrient supply through

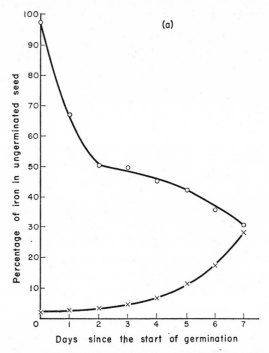

FIG. 44 (a). Movement of salts in germinating seedlings
Iron content of cotyledons (O—O) and axis (×—×) of kidney bean seedlings during the first week of germination (redrawn from Biddulph, 1951);

the surface of the leaves, and the same is probably true of certain aerial epiphytes of tropical and subtropical regions which grow attached to inanimate objects. Even terrestrial plants which do not normally absorb much salt in this way will readily do so when salt solutions are applied to the leaf surface. This has led to the important agricultural and horticultural technique of foliar feeding (Blattdüngung) of macro- and micro-nutrients to crops. Interest has been aroused in the possibility that additional amounts of essential elements may be supplied more economically as sprays on the foliage than by application to the soil. The extensive dissemination of insecticides, fungicides and weed-killers from the air can be con-

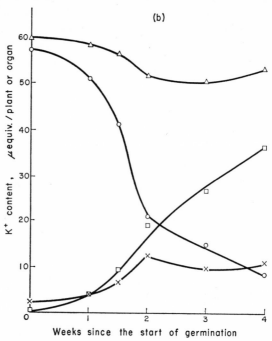

FIG. 44 (b).   Movement of salts in germinating seedlings
Potassium content of cotyledons (○—○), shoots (□—□), roots (×—×) and whole plants (△—△) of *Pisum sativum* during growth for 4 weeks at 20 °C in the dark in the absence of supplied potassium (Sutcliffe, unpublished).

veniently combined with that of fertilizers. The fact that mineral salts can be presented in this way when the crop is already growing actively ensures that a high percentage of the salt is absorbed and there are minimum opportunities for losses by leaching. Since air temperature rather than soil temperature controls foliar absorption, it is said that application of mineral salts to leaves has a decided advantage over conventional practice with crops growing in cold climates where the air temperature rises in spring much more rapidly than that of the soil.

Amongst factors affecting foliar absorption, the surface area, shape and arrangement of leaves are of foremost importance. In general, leaves of typical monocotyledonous plants retain solutes less readily and hence absorb them less efficiently than do leaves of many dicotyledons. Before salts can enter a plant, the leaf surface must be wetted and the ease with which this can be achieved depends on, among other things, the fat content of the cuticle, the number of appendages and the surface tension of the applied solution. Fogg (1947) found great differences in the wettability of leaves depending on the species examined, the age of the leaf and its water content. Roberts *et al.* (1948) demonstrated the presence of layers of pectinaceous material in the cuticle of apple leaves which are continuous with similar layers in the walls of the epidermal cells below. It is possible that solutes can move along these pathways into the leaf. Although hairs tend to decrease the wettability of a leaf because they trap air bubbles, they increase the amount of solution held at the leaf surface once wetting is achieved. Addition of surface-active substances or wetting agents to the solution promotes the absorption of salts under some conditions. Uptake is clearly related to the length of time an aqueous solution remains in contact with the leaf surface, and therefore it is affected by factors such as air movements, temperature and humidity which influence the rate of evaporation.

There is some controversy about the importance of stomata as ports of entry of solutes into leaves. Crafts (1933) claimed that the pores of fully-open stomata are generally small enough for surface tension to prevent penetration of aqueous solutions. In support of this, Rodney (1952) found no correlation between the number and condition of stomata and the rate of entry of calcium nitrate and ammonium sulphate into leaves of apple trees. Tiny drops of solution do sometimes penetrate stomata directly when a heavy spray is applied, leading to infiltration of the sub-stomatal spaces, and increased absorption. According to F. M. Scott (1950) a layer of cuticle commonly covers the inner walls of leaf epidermis and the walls of mesophyll cell, adjoining stomatal cavities, so that entry through the stomata does not necessarily absolve the nutrients from traversing cuticularized cell walls.

Most investigators have found that, other things being equal, nutrients penetrate more rapidly into young than into mature leaves. Structural differences, for example, in the cuticle and epidermis may be important in this connexion, but Oland and Opland (1956) proposed that a difference in metabolic activity may also be involved. They suggested that magnesium ions are taken up by leaves mainly in exchange for metabolically-produced hydrogen ions, and a diurnal variation in organic acid production may account for the more effective penetration of magnesium ions when salts are sprayed on to leaves in the evening than in the early afternoon.

The rapid initial absorption of cations by leaves and the ease of its reversal suggest that at least a part of uptake is by adsorption-exchange with the cuticle and cell walls behaving as a cation exchange membrane (cf. p. 104). Anion absorption on the other hand is almost entirely irreversible, and judging by its sensitivity to metabolic inhibitors, seems to be more completely dependent on active absorption than is the uptake of cations.

Some of the salt absorbed by leaves after foliar application, is retained, especially when the leaf is young, and the remainder is exported in the phloem. The mechanism of transport of salts from the leaf has been studied particularly by Biddulph. He showed (Biddulph, 1941) that when phosphate labelled with ^{32}P was injected into the phloem of a bean (*Phaseolus vulgaris*) leaf, movement into the stem occurred more rapidly during the hours of daylight than at night with a maximum rate at about 10 a.m. and a minimum about 12 hr later. Transport in the stem was at first predominantly in the downward direction, but some of the tracer eventually migrated across into the xylem and then began to move upwards. Using a technique similar to that employed by Stout and Hoagland (see p. 122), Biddulph and Markle (1944) were able to distinguish more exactly between phloem and xylem transport, and rates of transport in phloem exceeding 20 cm/hr were observed. Biddulph (1959) showed by radioautography of stem and petiole sections that sulphate and phosphate injected into a vein or sprayed on to a leaf moves out in the phloem. The phloem of a vascular bundle did not seem to behave as a single unit, since some sieve tubes became radioactive whereas neighbouring ones did not.

A discussion of the mechanism of phloem transport is beyond the scope of this monograph. For accounts of this problem you are referred to the recent reviews by Crafts (1951), Arisz (1952), Esau *et al.* (1957), Swanson (1959) and Zimmerman (1960).

G. EXCRETION OF SALTS

Salts are lost from various organs of the plant by both passive and active processes. Appreciable amounts are leached from roots, for example, when they are transferred from salt solutions to distilled water. Most of this salt is presumably washed from the free space of the tissue, but some is lost more slowly from cytoplasm and vacuoles. Such losses are probably due entirely to passive processes —at least no evidence of active excretion by roots has yet been obtained.

Salts are likewise leached from leaves and an investigation by Tamm (1951) revealed that certain forest mosses get most of their cations from the leaves of trees which are leached *in situ*. Xylem sap is exuded under pressure via stomata (guttation), and washed away by rain. If the rain water has an acid reaction, metallic cations may also be removed from the leaf through the cuticle by exchange for hydrogen ions. The well-known "chalk glands" of *Saxifragaceae* consist of modified stomata, from which a calcium-rich guttation fluid is exuded. This evaporates in air and a deposit of calcium carbonate remains. The term "gland" is more correctly restricted to structures in halophytic plants which excrete salts actively. The functioning of such glands is discussed in Chapter 9.

For further reading

BIDDULPH, O. (1959). Translocation of Inorganic Solutes. In *Plant Physiology— A Treatise*. (Ed. F. C. Steward). (Vol. II, Chap. 6 pp. 553–603). Academic Press, New York.

HOAGLAND, D. R. (1944). Upward movement and distribution of inorganic solutes in the plant. In *Lectures on the inorganic nutrition of Plants*, Chapter 4, pp. 72–103. Chronica Botanica, Waltham, Mass.

RUSSELL, R. S. and BARBER, D. A. (1960). The relationship between salt uptake and the absorption of water by intact plants. *Ann. Rev. Plant Physiol.* **11**, 127–40.

STENLID, G. (1958). Salt losses and redistribution of salts in higher plants. *Encycl. Plant Physiol.* **4**, 615–37.

STEWARD, F. C. (1954). Salt accumulation in plants. A. Reconsideration of the role of growth and metabolism. B. Salt accumulation in the plant body. *Symp. Soc. Exp. Biol.* **8**, 393–406.

CHAPTER 8

THE SOIL AS A SOURCE OF MINERAL SALTS

The multiphase system which the investigator of
plant nutrition explores is that of the soil-plant-
atmosphere with its innumerable interrelations and
interactions. Inherent in the green plant itself are all
the complexities common to living organisms, and to
these must be added the complexities of the soil
medium in which the plant is anchored and finds some
of the substances essential for its nourishment.

D. R. HOAGLAND.
Lectures on the Inorganic Nutrition of Plants
(1944).

A. INTRODUCTION

AN EARLY view of plant nutrition, dating from the time of Aristotle,
was that food materials were absorbed in an elaborated form from
the soil. This "humus theory", discredited by Van Helmont in the
seventeenth century (see p. 1), was not entirely disproved until
more than 100 years later, when it was demonstrated by solution
culture experiments that neither a supply of organic matter, nor the
insoluble mineral particles are essential for plant growth. Since
those days, the role of the soil as a source of plant nutrients has been
further investigated, and it is known that salts exist in a number of
different states in the soil, which can be conveniently classified under
three headings:

(i) water-soluble salts dissolved in the soil solution,

(ii) sparingly soluble or insoluble substances containing
exchangeable ions, and

(iii) insoluble substances, from which ions are not readily
obtained by exchange reactions.

Salts present in the soil solution are readily available to plants, and are also easily removed from soil by leaching. Exchangeable and non-exchangeable ions in soil are not so immediately available but they represent a large reservoir of mineral salts from which ions are slowly released into the soil solution. As a result, soil remains fertile for a long time in spite of the continual depletion of the soil solution through absorption by plants and leaching by rainfall.

B. THE SOIL SOLUTION

The soil solution comprises water and dissolved substances held in the soil against gravitational forces, but displaceable by liquids or by gas under pressure. Burd and Martin (1924) forced water under pressure through a tall column of soil, and collected the effluent in small aliquots. The first few samples had a similar composition and these were taken to be uncontaminated soil solution. The concentrations of various ions in solutions obtained in this way from a cultivated soil are given in Table 13A. It can be seen that the concentration of certain ions, particularly potassium, nitrate and phosphate was low, and this is characteristic of many soil solutions. The data of Table 13A show also that the concentration of salts in the soil solution decreases during the course of a growing season, and increases when the ground remains fallow.

The composition of soil solutions varies considerably between different soils, depending mainly on the nature of the parent material from which the soil was formed and the vegetation it supports (Table 13B). Saline and non-saline clay soils yield solutions which are especially rich in calcium, sodium and chloride, whereas in loams the soil solution tends to contain less of these ions relative to the amount of potassium present. Even in phosphorus-rich soils, the soil solution seldom contains more than about 1 part per million of this element. In a particular soil, the concentration of soil solution tends to be inversely proportional to the moisture content of the soil. This relationship holds particularly well for ions such as nitrate and chloride which are present in soil mainly in the dissolved state. The concentration of phosphate is more independent of soil moisture content, presumably because the soil solution is nearly saturated with rather insoluble phosphates, and when it is diluted more salt goes into solution from the solid phase. As soil moisture content is reduced, the concentrations of potassium and sodium in the soil solution tend to increase to a relatively smaller extent than do the concentrations of chloride, nitrate or calcium, suggesting that the amount of univalent cations in solution decreases with increasing concentration, through equilibration with the solid phase. At very low soil moisture content, the concentrations of all ions except phosphate increase with decreasing volume of soil

TABLE 13. THE COMPOSITION OF SOIL SOLUTIONS.

A. Analyses of soil solutions displaced from a cropped soil in California at the beginning and end of one growing season and at the beginning of the next. (Burd and Martin, 1924).

Date	m eq./l. of displaced solution							
	NO_3	HCO_3	SO_4	PO_4	Ca	Mg	Na	K
30.4.1923	2·23	1·75	7·10	0·05	6·75	3·70	2·35	1·10
4.4.1923	0·21	2·88	4·36	0·008	4·00	1·89	1·13	0·59
28.4.1924	2·71	2·33	9·56	0·04	8·45	4·52	2·39	1·26

B. Analyses of soil solutions extracted from 4 soils. (Reitemeier and Richards, 1944).

Soil	m eq./l. of displaced solution								Moisture content (%)
	NO_3	HCO_3	Cl	SO_4	Ca	Mg	Na	K	
Saline clay (Imperial)	89	3·8	155·4	19·4	786·8	319·0	563·8	2·9	27·2
Non-saline clay (Gila adobe)	—	3·8	15·2	26·1	23·6	6·0	22·7	1·0	28·9
Loam (Millville)	—	5·4	3·1	1·3	13·6	6·8	1·3	0·24	13·6
Sandy loam	17·6	3·5	3·3	2·9	18·2	4·0	3·3	7·7	10·4

solution more rapidly than can be accounted for, assuming that all the water in the soil contains dissolved salts. It appears that some of the soil water, bound to colloidal particles, is unavailable to salts.

C. EXCHANGEABLE IONS

1. *Anion Exchange Capacity*

Anions are present only to a limited extent, in undissolved, but exchangeable, forms attached to soil particles. Since they are held by positive charges originating from basic groups, e.g. in various clays, the anion exchange capacity of soils increases with decreasing pH (cf. Fig. 9, p. 38). It varies greatly for different anions; chloride and nitrate are bound very slightly by most soils, except in extremely acid conditions, whereas phosphate is adsorbed at high as well as at low pH values. Sulphate is weakly adsorbed by most soils even at low pH but appreciable adsorption occurs when the soil is rich in hydrated oxides of iron or aluminium, because sulphate can apparently displace hydroxyl ions from these substances. Phosphate competes strongly with sulphate for these sites.

2. *Cation Exchange Capacity*

The "base exchange" or "cation exchange" capacity of a soil is much greater than its anion exchange capacity and is of much greater significance in plant nutrition. Cation exchange capacity (C.E.C.), that is, the number of exchangeable cations in a given amount of soil, ranges from 1–2 m eq./100 g dry weight for sandy soils, to 60 m eq, or more for clay soils, and for soils rich in organic matter (Table 14). C.E.C. increases with increasing pH as the exchangeable ions are held at negatively charged sites on amphoteric soil colloids.

The bulk of the exchangeable cations in soils consists of Ca^{++} $Mg,^{++}$ K^+ and $Na,^+$ and of these, calcium ions usually predominate in non-saline soils (Table 14). Hydrogen ions may comprise a considerable proportion of the exchangeable cations in acid soils, and this leads to infertility, since other essential cations are displaced into the soil solution where they are subject to leaching. Of the major exchangeable ions, calcium and magnesium are bound most firmly, and sodium is most weakly adsorbed. The latter is thus particularly liable to be leached from soil and this is the reason for its considerable accumulation in the sea.

An equilibrium is maintained between exchangeable ions and the soil solution, and if this is disturbed, for example, by the absorption of salts from the soil solution by plants, desorption of exchangeable ions occurs until an equilibrium is re-established. In this way, exchangeable ions become available to plants.

D.   NON-EXCHANGEABLE IONS

The greater part of the mineral salts occurring in soil is present in the form of relatively insoluble substances from which ions do not readily exchange. Montmorillonite minerals for example, contain large amounts of potassium in a non-exchangeable form, and apatite consists of insoluble calcium phosphates. Such substances are slowly transformed under natural conditions by the complex sequence of changes known as "weathering", and this leads gradually to increased solubility and exchangeability of ions. The rate of weathering varies greatly for different minerals, and is affected by pH, soil moisture content and temperature. Contact between plant roots and soil increases the rate at which ions are

TABLE 14. CATION EXCHANGE CAPACITIES (C.E.C.) AND THE AMOUNTS OF MAJOR EXCHANGEABLE IONS IN VARIOUS SOILS.
(From Wiklander, 1958).

Soil	C.E.C. (m eq./100 g)	% of Total				pH
		Ca	Mg	K	Na	
Chernozem (Russia)	56·1	84·3	11·0	1·6	3·0	7·0
Dutch soils	38·3	79·0	13·0	2·0	6·0	7·0
Californian soils	20·3	65·6	26·3	5·5	2·6	7·0
Swedish soils { unlimed	17·3	72·3	23·6	2·7	1·4	6·0
limed	20·0	84·2	13·4	1·8	0·6	7·0

rendered more exchangeable, both by mechanical effects which cause the break-up of larger soil particles, and by chemical effects of carbonic acid, and organic acids, produced by the roots.

It is well known that many clay soils are able to supply sufficient potassium for the indefinite growth of natural vegetation, if not of crops. This is possible because an equilibrium exists between non-exchangeable potassium, exchangeable potassium and the soil solution. If a soil becomes low in dissolved or exchangeable potassium, non-exchangeable ions are gradually released and become available to plants. Conversely, some fixation of potassium in non-exchangeable forms occurs when potassium-containing fertilizers are added to potassium-depleted soils.

E. Absorption of Ions from Soil

1. *Anions*

As far as is known, anions are absorbed by plants almost entirely from the soil solution. A reservoir of certain anions is present as insoluble substances but this is not true of nitrate. During the growing season, soils normally show a decline in the amount of soluble nitrogen compounds present, and this is followed by a slow replacement, through nitrogen fixation and the breakdown of organic substances. The periodic growing of legumes, which are symbiotically associated with nitrogen-fixing bacteria, followed by "digging-in" of the crop ("green manuring") is a well-known method of increasing the available nitrogen in soils. Application of nitrogen-containing fertilizers is essential for the maintenance of high crop yields on arable land under modern agricultural practice.

Phosphorus exists in soils mainly as insoluble phosphates from which it can be released to some extent by other anions. Dean and Rubins (1947) found that the effectiveness with which various anions cause release of phosphate was in the order: hydroxyl > citrate > fluoride > tartarate > arsenate > acetate. Soil micro-organisms assist in rendering phosphate available for plants by the organic acids they excrete, and also by causing enzymatic degradation of organic phosphorus-containing substances such as nucleic acids, phosphatides and phytin.

The concentration of phosphate in soil solutions is so low that doubts have been expressed whether plants can absorb it quickly enough from this source alone to sustain normal growth. Tidmore (1930) showed, however, by experiments involving flowing culture solutions, that even rapidly growing plants can absorb adequate amounts of phosphate from media containing as little as 0·5 parts per million of soluble phosphorus. Phosphorus uptake by *Zea mays* was increased when the concentration of the solution was raised to 1 part per million, but growth was not improved. If phosphate is absorbed solely from the soil solution, the solution must be replenished frequently during growth of a crop. Stout and Overstreet (1950) calculated from experiments with potted plants that the soil solution might need to be completely recharged with phosphate 10 times/day during the growing season to support the growth of some crops.

A large part of the soluble phosphates added to soils as fertilizers is quickly rendered insoluble, mainly by precipitation as hydrated aluminium, iron and calcium phosphates. The addition of chelating agents to phosphate fertilizers reduces the amount of phosphate fixed in non-exchangeable forms, presumably by removing calcium and heavy metal ions from solution. The presence of legumes which tend to absorb calcium rapidly, can under some conditions promote the growth of associated plants, for example, cereals in phosphate-deficient soils, for the same reason.

Sulphates form the most important source of sulphur for plants. Most of the sulphates present in soil are relatively insoluble, and

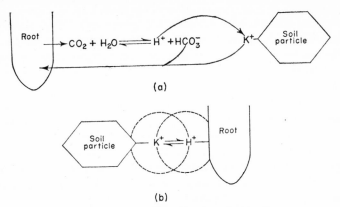

Fig. 45. Absorption of cations from soil
a. The carbon dioxide hypothesis; b. The contact exchange hypothesis.

are not immediately available, but gypsum ($CaSO_4 \cdot 2H_2O$) which is sparingly soluble, weathers rapidly to yield sulphate ions. Sulphides tend to be insoluble but they are gradually brought into solution by oxidation through weathering, and by the activity of sulphur-oxidizing bacteria.

2. Cations

a. Carbon dioxide hypothesis. Plants possess the capacity to facilitate cation release from the solid state, as is shown by the well-known ability of roots to etch the surface of marble (Sachs, 1875). An early suggestion was that respiratory carbon dioxide released from roots reacts with water to produce carbonic acid, which diffuses to the surface of the soil particle (Fig. 45a). Here exchange

takes place between hydrogen ions and adsorbed cations, as a result
of which the latter enter the soil solution. The released cations then
diffuse to the root surface where they are absorbed either by exchange
for hydrogen ions or in association with anions. Overstreet *et al.*
(1942) observed that cations are absorbed in excess of anions by
barley roots from clay suspensions and concluded that organic acids
synthesized in the root are the ultimate source of hydrogen ions
replacing other cations on the clay particles. Their observations do
not preclude the possibility that bicarbonate ions are taken up in
association with cations and converted to organic acid anions within
the plant, at least from alkaline soils (cf. p. 52).

As an argument against the carbon dioxide hypothesis, Elgabaly
et al. (1943) demonstrated that under comparable conditions barley
roots absorb more potassium and zinc from montmorillonite clay
suspensions than from kaolinite clay suspensions, whereas release of
cations from the two clays by carbonic acid solutions was greater
from kaolinite than from montmorillonite. Nevertheless it seems
likely that this mechanism plays an important part in the release of
exchangeable ions from the solid phase into soil solutions.

b. Contact exchange. There is some evidence that cations can
exchange between roots and soil without intervention of the soil
solution. Devaux (1916) drew attention to the cation exchange
properties of roots and suggested that roots and soil particles, being
in intimate contact with one another, might form a single colloidal
system through which cations move by exchange. Jenny and
Overstreet (1938) elaborated the idea of "contact exchange" as
follows: adsorbed ions are not held rigidly at the site of adsorption,
but vibrate around this point, thus occupying from time to time a
finite volume—the so-called "oscillation volume". When the
oscillation volumes of two adsorbed ions overlap, contact exchange
can occur (Fig. 45b).

Evidence for direct exchange of cations between roots and the
solid phase of soil has been demonstrated in experiments with
radioactive isotopes. Hoagland (1944) describes an experiment of
Martin and Overstreet in which radioactive rubidium ions were
added to the soil under investigation, and the soil was then leached
with a solution of a calcium salt to remove radioactivity from the
soil solution and from some of the sites at which rubidium ions were
held in an exchangeable condition. Subsequently barley plants were

grown in the leached soil and they absorbed significant amounts of rubidium. Other experiments show that plants can absorb from soil potassium which is difficult to remove by leaching. Leaching of a soil with carbonic acid for 10 days yielded only half as much potassium as that absorbed in the same period by rye plants.

Prolonged absorption of metallic cations in exchange for hydrogen ions through contact exchange might be achieved by continuous synthesis of acidic colloidal substances (for example, pectic and pectinic acids) at the root surface, coupled with growth to bring them into contact with fresh particles of soil. Alternatively, after exchange has occurred, the adsorbed cation at the root surface may be transferred elsewhere, and replaced at the adsorption site by a hydrogen ion which can participate in another exchange reaction with the soil.

The presence of exchangeable hydrogen ions at root surfaces can be detected either by displacing them into solution with other cations, or by measurements of the electrokinetic potential difference between root surface and external solution. Lundegårdh (1954) demonstrated with a cathode ray oscilloscope that whole wheat roots immersed in a dilute salt solution have a negative electro-kinetic potential of about 60 mV. The rapidity with which the potential difference alters when the composition of the medium is changed suggests that the site of the electrical charge concerned is the root surface. The potential can be attributed to dissociation of acidic substances, and it behaves essentially as a Donnan potential (p. 34). In the absence of metallic cations in the medium, the free acids present at the root surface cause it to behave as a hydrogen electrode. The measured potential is related to the logarithm of $[H_i^+]/[H_o^+]$ where $[H_i^+]$ and $[H_o^+]$ represent the concentrations of hydrogen ions in the root surface and in the medium respectively. If a neutral salt is present in the solution, other cations exchange with hydrogen ions and the potential is lowered by an amount which is approximately proportional to the logarithm of the salt concentration.

The maximum number of readily exchangeable cations (including hydrogen ions) held by a given weight of roots (cation exchange capacity) shows wide variation between different species (Table 15). In general dicotyledonous roots have higher C.E.C. values than do those of monocotyledons, while species with thick mucilaginous roots have a greater cation exchange capacity than those with fine fibrous roots. On a surface area basis, the C.E.C. of thick roots may be 10–100 times that of thin ones.

There is no clear relationship between C.E.C. values and the rate at which plants absorb salts, but species with a high C.E.C. value tend to absorb more calcium relative to univalent ions from a given soil. Peas, for example, were found to take up 2–3 times as much calcium as barley plants from a sodium/calcium bentonite clay, but

TABLE 15. CATION EXCHANGE CAPACITY OF ROOTS.
(From Drake, Vengris and Colby, 1951).

Plant	C.E.C. (m eq/100 g dry wt.)
A. **Dicotyledons**	
Delphinium ajacis	94·0
Glycine max (soya)	65·1
Lactuca sativa	65·1
Lupinus angustifolius	53·3
Pisum sativum	49·6
Solanum tuberosum	38·1
Gossypium sp.	36·1
Chenopodium album	25·0
B. **Monocotyledons**	
Festuca pratensis (*elatior*)	30·4
Allium cepa	29·5
Avena sativa	22·8
Agropyron repens	19·8
Hordeum vulgare	12·3
Panicum miliaceum	12·2
Triticum sp.	9·0

only 20–25 per cent as much sodium. This is probably related to the preferential binding of calcium rather than sodium to the exchange sites in the free space of roots, which causes relatively greater amounts of calcium that sodium to be available at the surface of the cytoplasm in roots with a high C.E.C. value than in those with low. The ratio of bivalent to univalent ions adsorbed passively in the cell walls, does not, however, determine the proportions in which these ions are absorbed by the root system as a whole. The ratio of potassium to calcium absorption by barley and oat plants, for example, may be as high as 20 and 60 respectively, indicating that

there is preferential absorption of univalent ions from the cation exchange sites.

Several objections have been raised to the contact exchange hypothesis, but none have seriously weakened it. It has been suggested, for example, that the surface area of soil particles in contact with the absorbing region of a root is too small to permit absorption by contact exchange to an appreciable extent. However, at the microscopic and sub-microscopic level, colloidal clay particles present a large surface for cation exchange in close proximity to the

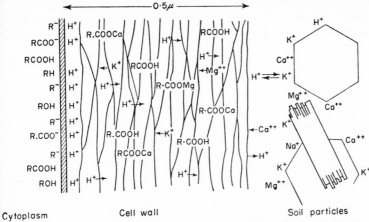

Fig. 46. Diagrammatic representation of cross section of a root hair cell wall showing relationship with cytoplasm and soil particles and direction of movement of cations (modified from Frey-Wyssling, 1945).

root surface. Jenny (1951) calculated that 1 mm² of root surface can make contact with 10^8 clay particles each carrying 6000–7000 exchangeable cations. A second objection is that the presence of an inert cellulose cell wall between the clay particle and cytoplasmic surface prevents the two systems from making intimate enough contact with one another for direct exchange to occur. However, the cell wall has a definite exchange capacity, and together with excreted mucilage, it can effectively bridge the gap between exchange sites in soil and cytoplasm (Fig. 46).

3. *Micronutrients*

It is a somewhat surprising fact that in spite of the extremely small amounts of various trace elements required by plants, their availability in the soil often limits growth. This may happen even when the soil contains adequate amounts of the element in question. Iron and manganese, for example, are precipitated as insoluble oxides at alkaline pH values and this may lead to micronutrient deficiencies in calcareous soils. Some iron is still available in alkaline soils in the form of soluble complex salts of humic acids, and this may suffice for the growth of some, but not all, species. Some calcifuge plants, e.g. rhododendrons, grow badly in calcareous soils because they suffer from iron deficiency. Improved growth of these plants in such soils can sometimes be obtained by supplying additional iron in the form of soluble chelate compounds, such as iron E.D.T.A. (Fig. 10, p. 39).

Manganese deficiency is likewise more pronounced at alkaline pH values, but it is observed also in acid soils when a large amount of organic matter is present. This is apparently due to the formation of insoluble complexes with organic substances, which are not absorbed, and from which manganese is not easily released. Manganese toxicity generally occurs on very acid soils and can often be remedied by liming. Limitation of plant growth as a result of copper deficiency is best known for cereals growing in soils which are rich in organic materials, where stable complexes between copper and organic substances are formed.

Zinc deficiency symptoms seem to be due more often to unavailability of the element in the soil, than to its absence. Absorption of zinc is reduced with increasing pH, and this is attributed to a reduction in the concentration of zinc in the soil solution. Healthy crops can be grown in neutral soils, low in zinc, if fresh organic material is added as an available source of zinc. Decomposition of the organic materials into humus seems to render the zinc unavailable, again by formation of insoluble complexes.

It is well known that application of lime to soils enhances the development of boron deficiency symptoms in boron-deficient soils, but the reason for this is still in doubt. Drake *et al.* (1941) concluded that boron is not adsorbed by clay or organic matter at alkaline pH values, or rendered insoluble by calcium. In contrast the growth of crops in molybdenum-deficient soils is improved by liming, and this is due to increased availability of molybdates with increasing pH.

For further reading

BEAR, F. E. (1955). *Chemistry of the Soil* Reinhold, New York.

BROYER, T. C. and STOUT, P. R. (1959). The macronutrient elements. *Ann. Rev. Plant Physiol.* **10**, 277–300.

FRIED, M. and SHAPIRO, R. E. (1961). Soil-plant relationships in ion uptake. *Ann. Rev. Plant Physiol.* **12**, 91–112.

STOUT, P. R. and OVERSTREET, R. (1950). Soil chemistry in relation to inorganic nutrition of plants. *Ann. Rev. Plant Physiol.* **1**, 305–42.

WIKLANDER, L. (1958). The soil. *Encycl. Plant Physiol.* **IV**, 118–69.

CHAPTER 9

SALT TOLERANCE

Enough is as good as a feast . . . too much of a good
thing is good for nothing.
THEODORE HOOK.

A. SALT TOLERANCE OF GLYCOPHYTES

THE GROWTH of most plants is retarded when the salt content of
the soil exceeds a rather low value, and to these salt-sensitive plants
the term "glycophytes" or "glyptophytes" is applied. Halophytes
(Gr. halas = salt), on the other hand, grow habitually on soils or in
solutions containing a high concentration of salts, and are seldom,
if ever found elsewhere. The salt sensitivity of crops is of some
commercial importance as well as of academic interest since yields
are reduced when the salt content of soils exceeds an optimum
value. The increasing irrigation of crops in the field, as well as in
hot-houses with tap and river water which is rich in salts, is now-
adays rendering the problem more acute. It is said that crops on
25–30 per cent of the arable land in the United States of America
suffer to some extent from salt excess. One of the important stages
in the reclamation of land from the sea, as practised, for example, in
the Netherlands, is the leaching of salt from the soil until its concentration is sufficiently low, to allow the growth of satisfactory crops.

Deleterious effects of high-salt soils on the growth of plants may
be attributed to two separate factors:

(i) reduced water absorption because of the high external
osmotic pressure, and

(ii) specific effects of certain ions on metabolism when they are
present in the medium at a high concentration.

It is not easy to distinguish between these possibilities, but attempts
have been made to do so by comparing growth of plants, placed
with their roots, in iso-osmotic aqueous solutions of different

149

composition. Gauch and Wadleigh (1944) obtained evidence for the importance of an asmotic factor in kidney beans (*Phaseolus vulgaris*) by their observation that similar inhibitions of growth are obtained by supplying osmotically equivalent amounts of either sodium chloride, sodium sulphate or calcium chloride in the medium. These solutions seemed to have no effects on growth which could be attributed to individual ions. Magnesium chloride and sulphate solutions, however, caused greater depression of growth than did the other solutions of comparable osmotic pressure indicating that magnesium ions have a specific inhibitory effect independent of osmotic pressure. All species do not react in the same way to excess of a particular salt. Some species of beans and peaches, for example, are more sensitive to solutions containing high concentration of chloride than sulphate, whereas in flax and cotton, the situation is reversed.

It is evident from simple osmotic considerations that when the concentration of the medium is increased, water absorption is reduced and growth tends to diminish. To some extent, the influence of high external osmotic pressure is offset by an increase in the osmotic pressures of the root cells through increased absorption of salts (Table 16), but this is insufficient to prevent a gradual decline in the difference between the diffusion pressure deficit (DPD) of the cell sap and that of the soil solution. Water absorption and growth presumably stop when the DPD of water in the medium is about equal to the diffusion pressure deficit of that in the vacuolar sap in cells of the root. At this point the cells are nearly flaccid, that is, the wall pressure approaches zero, and thus the osmotic pressures of the cell sap and medium also tend towards equality. The presence of a high DPD in the shoot does not seem to be effective in maintaining an adequate supply of water to the plant in the absence of a difference of DPD between the root cells and external medium.

There is, however, no apparent correlation between the salt tolerance of different species, and the DPD of the cell sap in roots grown under natural conditions (Table 16). The ability of the root cells to raise the osmotic pressure of the vacuolar sap and maintain it at an adequate level under high salt conditions is of greater importance. Another factor is the transpiration rate of the plant, since water loss must be more than replaced by absorption before growth is possible. Shallow-rooted plants, and those with large shoot-to-root ratios, that is, plants with poor water absorptive capacity in relation to transpiration, tend to exhibit poor salt tolerance. A low shoot-to-root ratio seems to be one of the adaptations of some halophytes to saline habitats. As may be expected, conditions leading to high transpiration, e.g. high light intensity, and low humidity, may induce salt damage at concentrations which have no deleterious effects under conditions favouring low rates of

TABLE 16. SALT TOLERANCE (OSMOTIC PRESSURE OF SODIUM CHLORIDE GIVING 50 PER CENT REDUCED GROWTH) AND THE OSMOTIC PRESSURE OF THE EXPRESSED SAP FROM THE LEAVES AND ROOTS, OF VARIOUS SPECIES, PLACED WITH THEIR ROOTS IN MEDIA OF DIFFERENT OSMOTIC PRESSURES.
(Abbreviated from Bernstein and Hayward, 1958).

Plant	Salt tolerance	Part of the plant	O.P. of nutrient medium				
			0	1·25	2·50	3·75	5·00
Onion	1·25	Leaves	10·4	8·6	11·3		
		Roots	3·6	4·1	4·7		
Cucumber	1·25	Leaves	6·9	6·8	8·1	9·4	
		Roots	2·9	2·6	3·4	2·9	
Pea	2	Leaves	10·5	14·2	16·8		
		Roots	5·1	10·4	9·3	4·7	
Pepper	3·75	Leaves	12·1	12·4	16·7		13·7
		Roots	5·4	5·5	5·4	5·8	7·0
Bean	4	Leaves	8·3	9·1	9·3	11·5	11·4
		Roots	3·9	4·0	3·6	3·0	3·2
Lettuce	4	Leaves	5·3	6·3	8·4	9·0	10·7
		Roots	3·0	3·4	3·9	4·4	6·6
Cabbage	4	Leaves	9·9	11·9	12·7	11·3	11·9
		Roots	3·3	3·9	5·1	4·2	4·6

transpiration. Finally, slow-growing species tend on the whole to be more salt-tolerant than those which grow rapidly.

The specific inhibitory effects on growth of ions at high concentrations are still not properly understood. Interference with the absorption of an essential element or with its functioning in the cytoplasm are among the possible causes. A high concentration of salt may adversely affect the activity of cytoplasm through an influence upon hydration and the effect of a particular ion at a high concentration can sometimes be counterbalanced by the presence of another with an opposing influence (ion antagonism). It has often been reported, for example, that sodium and calcium ions counteract one another in this way, a solution containing both these ions at high concentration having a smaller inhibitory influence than solutions containing either of the two separately (Osterhout, 1912).

There is some evidence that salt tolerance is related to the ability of plants to absorb potassium in competition with other cations. Bernstein and Ayers (1953) showed that in several varieties of carrot salinity, achieved by addition of calcium and sodium chlorides to the soil, increased the rate of absorption of calcium and depressed that of potassium. Those varieties which tended to absorb most calcium and least potassium at a given level of salinity gave relatively poorer yields than the others. It is not surprising, therefore, that, in some plants, salt tolerance can be improved by increasing the amount of potassium supplied relative to sodium and calcium.

Some species, e.g. beets, cotton and tomatoes, which are fairly tolerant of high concentrations of salts when grown in nutrient solutions, give poor yields in soils of comparable salinity. This is attributed to an effect of high salt content, particularly sodium ion concentration, on the physical condition of the soil. The soil becomes hard and compacted with consequent adverse effects of moisture conditions, aeration and resistance to root penetration. Salt-sensitive species, on the other hand, are commonly affected by salt concentrations which are without evident effect on soil texture and they tend to suffer less when grown in soil than in solution culture, presumably because soil exerts some buffering action, for example, by release of calcium, to moderate cation unbalance in the supplied solution.

B.   SUBMERGED HALOPHYTES

There are a number of plants which grow permanently submerged in salt water. These include many algae, mainly belonging to the Phaeophyceae and Rhodophyceae, and a few angiosperms including *Zostera maritima*. The salt content of the bathing medium ranges from that of brackish water which may be only a little more concentrated than fresh water, to that of some inland seas and lakes, e.g. the Dead Sea (Israel); Wadi Natrum (Egypt) and Salt Lake (U.S.A.) in which salt may reach a concentration of 10 per cent or more. Normal sea water contains about 3 per cent of salts, and its approximate composition is shown in Fig. 47.

A characteristic feature of marine halophytes is their capacity to accumulate potassium in preference to sodium from sea water (Table 17). Steward and Martin (1937) studied the effect of environ-

TABLE 17. SALT COMPOSITION OF SOME SEAWEEDS.
A. Ratios of potassium/sodium in sea-water and in some marine halophytes.
(From Bertrand and Perietzeanu, 1927).

Material	K^+/Na^+
Sea-water	0·04
Rhodymenia palmata	78·00
Ulva lactuca	10·45
Laminaria saccharina	6·37
Pelvetia canaliculata	1·46
Fucus serratus	0·85
Zostera maritima	1·15

B. The sap composition of *Valonia ventricosa* and *Valonia macrophysa* at Dry Tortugas, Florida.
(From Steward and Martin, 1937).

Species	Number of samples	Ion	Sap composition (g eq./l.)	
			Mean	Mean $\pm$ 2 $\times$ Standard error
V. ventricosa	62	K^+	0·591	0·595–0·587
		Na^+	0·043	0·046–0·040
		Cl^-	0·628	0·631–0·625
V. macrophysa	30	K^+	0·509	0·520–0·498
		Na^+	0·113	0·123–0·103
		Cl^-	0·624	0·628–0·620

mental conditions on the potassium and sodium content of species of *Valonia* growing at the Dry Tortugas, in Florida. They found that in general *V. macrophysa* exhibits a lower potassium to sodium ratio than *V. ventricosa* (Table 17b), but plants of *V. macrophysa* exposed to long daily periods of full sunlight exhibited a higher ratio than those growing in more shaded situations. The quantity of illumination does not seem to affect the cation ratio in *V. ventricosa* which normally grows more deeply submerged, and hence at lower light intensities than *V. macrophysa* but plants growing in smoother water tend to contain more potassium relative to sodium than those exposed to rough seas. There is tendency in both species for the potassium to sodium ratio to diminish with age.

The older physiologists, including Osterhout (see p. 76), believed that the low concentration of sodium relative to potassium in *Valonia* coenocytes is due to the slow rates at which sodium is

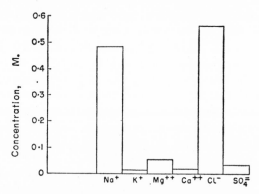

FIG. 47.   The approximate concentrations of the most abundant ions in
sea-water.

taken up. Another possibility is that the low internal sodium concentration is maintained at least partly by active extrusion such as has been demonstrated in *Ulva lactuca*. Scott and Hayward (1953, 1954) found that *Ulva* cells maintain a high potassium to sodium ratio only in the light, and when the thallus is transferred to darkness, potassium is gradually released and sodium taken up as respiratory substrates become depleted. Upon subsequent illumination, sodium is excreted and potassium accumulated until the normal cation balance is attained (Fig. 15b, p. 49). When a tissue has been leached of salt by prolonged washing in sucrose, isotonic with sea-water, and is then transferred to sea-water, the cells rapidly return to equilibrium by uptake of both potassium and sodium. The mechanisms of absorption of the two ions seem to be independent, because uptake of potassium is unaffected by the concentration of sodium in the medium. Differences in the sensitivity of the two mechanisms to metabolic inhibitors have also been noted. Sodium absorption seemed to be related particularly to metabolism of pyruvate, whereas potassium uptake was identified more closely with phosphorylation. The possible location of the absorption mechanisms in *Ulva* has already been discussed (Chapter 6, p. 103).

Seaweeds are obligate halophytes, that is, they not only tolerate a high concentration of salt but they appear to require it. Attempts to grow seaweeds in artificial sea-water, only a little different in composition from normal, have proved unsuccessful. Among submerged spermatophytes, *Zostera maritima* requires normal sea water for maximum growth whereas some species of *Myriophyllum* growing in brackish water have a small tolerance on either side of the optimum salt concentration, and *Ruppia spiralis* and *Ruppia maritima* can be adapted to growth in either salt or fresh water. Limits to the salt concentration that different submerged aquatic plants can tolerate largely controls the distribution of vegetation in river estuaries. The factors which determine whether an organism can live over a wide or narrow range of salt concentrations have been much less studied in plants than in animals, and further investigations would be welcome.

Kniep (1907) showed that the early growth of fertilized *Fucus* eggs depends on the presence of salt. The minimum salt requirement below which no development occurred was found to differ for different species, being a 0·8 per cent solution for *F. vesiculosus*, 1·0 per cent for *F. serratus*, and 1·5 per cent for *F. spiralis* which tends to grow more completely submerged than the other two species. Maximum germination of zygotes was observed in normal sea-water, and solutions containing higher concentrations of salt were inhibitory.

C. Terrestrial Halophytes

The inhabitants of salt marshes are an interesting group of plants which have intrigued ecologists and physiologists for many years. At least some of these plants will grow successfully and complete their life cycles only in the presence of high concentrations of salt (true halophytes). An example of this is the marsh samphire, *Salicornia stricta* (*herbacea*), which reaches maturity only in the presence of sodium chloride at about the same concentration as in sea-water. On the other hand, *Aster tripolium* and *Plantago maritima*

grow equally well as halophytes or glycophytes, but plants
accustomed to growing in soil with a low salt concentration grow
more slowly when subsequently transferred to a high-salt medium,
and vice versa.

One of the characteristic features of halophytes is the high
osmotic pressure of the cell sap, which is due mainly to high sodium
and chloride content (Fig. 48). As the concentration of sodium
chloride in the external medium increases, so does that in the cell

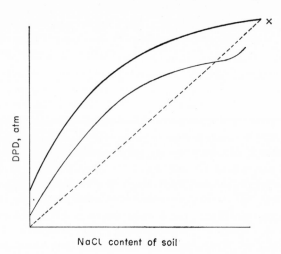

NaCl content of soil

Fig. 48. Diagrammatic representation of the relationship between sodium
chloride content of the soil and the diffusion pressure deficit (DPD) of the
cell sap in halophytes. Total DPD of cell sap=———; DPD due to sodium
chloride=———DPD of soil solution=– – – (redrawn from Adriani, 1958,
after Walter).

sap. Hill (1908) showed that the DPD of the sap in root hairs of
young plants of *Salicornia* was equivalent to a 5–6 per cent solution
of sodium chloride when these plants were grown in soil of which
the soil water contained about 3 per cent of chlorides. The root
hairs of *Salicornia* seedlings were found to have a corresponding
lower DPD after they had been bathed with weaker salt solutions.
Conversely when seedlings which had acquired a low DPD were
transferred to successively stronger solutions the root hairs were
found to regain a higher DPD. Very high osmotic pressures can be
attained in the cell sap of extreme halophytes. Ruhland (1912)

showed that when plants of *Limonium* (*Statice*) *gmelinii* were grown in solutions containing 10 per cent sodium chloride, the osmotic pressure of cell sap rose to 165 atm, and a plant of *Atriplex* sp. growing on a salt rich soil in Utah is said to have had sap with osmotic pressure exceeding 200 atm (Harris 1934). The growth rate of most halophytes is, however, retarded when the concentration of salt in the soil solution exceeds about 3 per cent.

Plants absorb relatively less salt from concentrated solutions than from dilute ones, so that the external osmotic pressure tends to increase relative to that of the cell sap as the concentration of salt in the medium increases. Theoretically, as external concentration is increased, a point X (Fig. 48) is reached at which the DPD of the plant and of the medium become equal, and water absorption then stops.

In the case of some halophytes, the salt concentration of the cell sap and its osmotic pressure continue to increase throughout the growing season. This group may be termed "accumulators" and *Juncus gerardi* can be cited as an example (Fig. 49a). Salt is absorbed throughout the vegetative period, and since the amount of water does not increase appreciably the osmotic pressure rises to a high value, but it does not apparently injure the plant. In other halophytes ("regulators") the osmotic pressure of the cell sap does not increase progressively with age even though salts are all the time being absorbed. The regulatory mechanism was investigated in leaves of *Iva oraria* by Steiner (1939), who showed that with increasing age there is a comparable increase in both salt and water content, so that the osmotic pressure of the cell sap remains approximately the same (Fig. 49b). Water absorption leads to swelling of the leaves and to a decrease in the surface area to volume ratio, i.e. there is the development of succulence. The degree of succulence in *Salicornia* plants has been shown to be related to the concentration of salts in the nutrient medium (Table 18). Salt-tolerant plants including the littoral species, *Beta maritima*, *Cakile maritima* and *Honkenya peploides*, as well as more ubiquitous species, such as *Solanum dulcamara* and *Plantago coronopus*, all have less fleshy leaves when growing inland than near the sea (Lesage, 1890).

The idea that halophytes are adapted to conditions of "physiological drought" was advanced by Schimper (1891) following his observation that when glycophytes are watered with saline solutions,

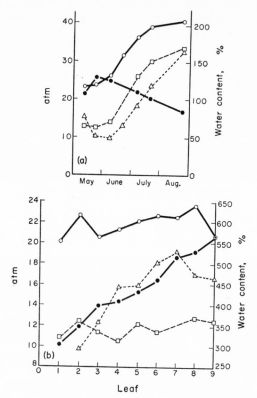

FIG. 49.   Regulation of salt concentration in halophytes

Total osmotic pressure (O—O); osmotic pressure of cell sap due to chlorides (□---□); osmotic pressure of cell sap due to sodium salts (△---△) and percentage water content (●—●) of a. *Juncus gerardi* during a growing season. Redrawn from Steiner (1934), and b. leaves of *Iva oraria* of different ages (leaf age increases in the series 1–9) (redrawn from Steiner, 1939).

their rate of transpiration is reduced. This led to the suggestion that halophytes have characteristically a low rate of transpiration, and that their structure is adapted for this purpose (cf the structure of xerophytes). However, Stahl (1894) demonstrated by the cobalt chloride paper method that halophytes can transpire surprisingly rapidly under favourable conditions, and Delf (1911) confirmed that in *Salicornia* sp. and *Sueda maritima*, the rate of transpiration from detached shoots can be as high, or even higher per unit of surface area than that of a typical glycophyte such as *Vicia faba*. Delf

(1912) pointed out that in the majority of halophytes, the transpiring surface is little protected from water loss, as there is often a thin cuticle and numerous, unsunken stomata.

In spite of these observations, it remains true that the arte of water loss by evaporation from succulent leaves is less than that from thin leaves on a fresh weight basis. Thus by the development of succulence, maximum storage of water and lowering of salt concentration is possible, with minimum increase in the rate of trans-

TABLE 18. SUCCULENCE (TOTAL WATER CONTENT/SURFACE AREA) IN *Salicornia stricta* (*herbacea*) GROWN IN VARIOUS SALT SOLUTIONS.
(Van Eijk, 1939).

Salt concentration (M)	NaCl	KCl	CaCl$_2$	NaNO$_3$
0	33±1	33±1	33±1	33±1
0·083	36±1·5	39±1·2	40±1	36±1·8
0·166	39±2·1	39±2·1	49±3	37±1·7
0·333	45±1·2	42±1		34±1·2
0·5	43±1·5	43±1·1		
0·666	51±4	42±1		

piration. Delf suggested that halophytes may supplement the water taken up by roots by absorption through the shoot from the damp atmosphere in which the plants often grow. Conditions which favour this process would of course, tend to reduce transpiration.

D. SALT GLANDS

Another mechanism by which salt concentration is regulated in halophytes is by elimination of ions from the shoot. To some extent, this occurs passively in guttation fluids which emerge from hydathodes under the influence of root pressure, and are dispersed by wind and rain. In addition, salt is actively excreted through the cuticle from epidermal cells, or by means of specialized "salt glands".

Salt glands vary in structure from the rather simple two-celled gland found in *Spartina townsendii* (Fig. 50b) and in some Indian halophytes (Mullan, 1931), to the intricate multicellular organs described by Ruhland (1912) on the leaves of *Limonium gmelinii* (Fig. 50a). In the latter, a single gland consists typically of a group

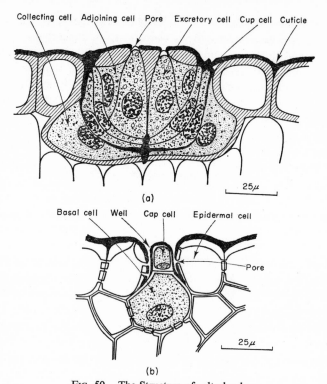

(a)

(b)

FIG. 50.   The Structure of salt glands

a. Salt gland from the leaf of *Limonium* (*Statice*) *gmelinii* (redrawn from Ruhland, 1912); b. Salt gland of *Spartina Townsendii* (redrawn from Skelding and Winterbotham, 1939).

of sixteen cells with large nuclei, dense cytoplasm and no chloroplasts or obvious vacuoles. Four large excretory cells are arranged centrally; closely associated with them are four smaller but similar "adjoining cells", and surrounding them are eight flattened cells forming a two-layered cup. The entire gland is enclosed by a rigid cuticle of irregular thickness which is penetrated by a small pore at the tip of each excretory cell. It is through these pores that the salt is excreted. Outside the gland proper, are four collecting cells communicating with the cup cells by protoplasmic connections through pores in the cuticle. The collecting cells serve as a link between the gland and underlying tissues of the leaf, and it is apparently through them that salts are transferred into the gland.

Ruhland estimated that there about 700 glands/mm^2 of leaf surface in *Limonium gmelinii* and these may excrete up to 1 ml of liquid per hour, containing perhaps 0·05 mg of sodium chloride. He found that the concentration of salt in the fluid excreted was about equal to that in the leaf tissue as a whole, and concluded that the glands do not necessarily perform osmotic work. His concept was that accumulation of salt takes place in the mesophyll of the leaf, and that a liquid rich in salt is squeezed out via the gland in some way under pressure (cf. guttation).

More recently, Arisz *et al.* (1955) have examined the mechanism of excretion by salt glands of another plant, *Limonium latifolium*. Like Ruhland, they made use of the earlier observation of Schtscherbak (1910) that glands attached to isolated fragments of leaf will continue to function. Leaf disks were rested on filter papers soaked in salt solutions, and kept in a water-saturated atmosphere to prevent evaporation of the excreted fluid. At the end of an experiment, the liquid accumulated on the upper surface of the disk was collected and analysed. By measuring also the volume of liquid excreted it was possible to calculate the concentration of salt. Under optimum conditions, the concentration of salt in the excreted fluid proved to be higher than the mean salt concentration of the leaf tissue, leading Arisz to the conclusion that the glands are capable of performing osmotic work. There is no reason to doubt that this is the case. Illumination of the leaf disk and increase of temperature increased the amount of fluid excreted, and metabolic inhibitors reduced it, but none of these treatments affected the concentration of salt in the exudate. Very little liquid was excreted under anaerobic conditions, and no chloride could be detected in it. When the osmotic pressure of the medium upon which the disks were placed was increased by addition of sucrose or magnesium sulphate, the amount of liquid excreted was reduced, but its concentration increased so that there was little effect on the total amount of salt present.

Arisz suggested that there is active accumulation of salts in the excretory cells of the gland. This tends to cause uptake of water from surrounding cells, and since the gland cannot swell appreciably owing to the enclosing cuticle, fluid is exuded under pressure through the pores. Since, on the basis of this hypothesis, the amount of liquid excreted depends on the pressure built up inside the gland, and this in turn is controlled by accumulation of salt, it is understandable that excretion is reduced by metabolic inhibitors. What is less clear is why the concentration of salts remains constant in these circumstances. If the mechanism operates in the manner suggested by Arisz, a reduced flow of liquid should be associated with lower concentration since the pressure developed, and hence the amount of liquid exuded, apparently depends on concentration. A more satisfactory explanation of Arisz's observations is that salt is actively excreted at the pore surfaces and this is followed by osmotic withdrawal of water. The reduced flow of more highly concentrated exudate when the tissue is in contact with a solution of high osmotic pressure can be adequately explained on the basis of either of the proposed hypotheses.

There are other kinds of glands on the leaves of some plants, for example, *Hypericum* sp. which excrete fragrant oils, and in these it is possible to see with a microscope that the oils appear first as minute globules in the protoplasm of the excretory cells. Later they can be seen as small droplets adhering to the outer surface of the gland. These observations suggest by analogy that the salt glands may function by the accumulation of salt in small vesicles within the cytoplasm of the leaf tissue. These are transferred into the excretory cells and discharged at the external protoplasmic surface in the vicinity of the pore. A further investigation of the mode of action of salt glands is urgently required, especially as it may shed important light on the mechanisms of salt absorption and movement in less specialized cells and tissues.*

For further reading

ARISZ, W. H. (1953). Significance of the symplasm theory for transport across the root. *Protoplasma*, **66**, 5–62.

ARNOLD, A. (1955). *Die Beutung der Chlorionen für die Pflanze, insbesondere deren physiologische Wirksamkeit. Eine monographische Studie mit Ausblicken auf das Halophytenproblem.* Gustav Fischer, Jena.

BERNSTEIN, L. and HAYWARD, H. E. (1958). Physiology of salt tolerance. *Ann. Rev. Plant Physiol.* **9**, 25–46.

HELDER, R. J. (1956). The loss of substances by cells and tissues (salt glands). *Encyclo. Plant Physiol.* **2**, 468–88.

* Note added in proof: An electron microscopic investigation undertaken by Dr. R. Barton at the instigation of the author has confirmed the presence of numerous vesicles in the cytoplasm of the excretory cells in salt glands of *Limonium*.

CHAPTER 10

EPILOGUE

There is nothing makes a man suspect much, more
than to know little.
BACON.
Essay XXXI, Of Suspicion

THE IDEA that salt absorption is mainly an active process has now
been firmly established for more than 30 years, but precise details
of the mechanism through which respiratory energy is used to bring
about accumulation is still far from certain. Many hypotheses have
been proposed but none has received widespread acceptance for one
reason or another. All have one feature in common, namely the
dependence at some stage on the formation of a specific complex
between the ion transported and an organic constituent of the
cytoplasm. There is great diversity of opinion about the likely
nature of the "carrier" substances. In my view, cytoplasmic proteins
may act as carriers, in the manner outlined below. There is not to my
knowledge any evidence to disprove this hypothesis, and much
which is consistent with it.

Salts diffuse as ions across the cellulose cell wall—the water-
filled spaces of which comprise the "free space" of the cell—to the
surface of the cytoplasm, where they become attached to protein
molecules located in the surface membrane. The ion-binding
capacity of proteins is best known in the case of enzymes, which
are the only proteins yet isolated from cytoplasm in a fairly natural
state, but doubtless other proteins possess the same ability. Whether
all the proteins which bind ions at the cell surface are in fact enzymes
is not yet certain but this is quite likely to be the case. As a result of
protein synthesis, new sites are created to which salts may be bound,
and uptake from the medium continues as long as newly synthesized
protein is being exposed at the external surface.

Cytoplasm is in a constant state of flow (cyclosis), which means

163

that the constituent proteins are mobile, and probably move periodically from the surface into the bulk of the cytoplasm carrying bound ions with them. Pinocytosis may play an important part in this process. Within the cytoplasm, proteins are continually being broken down and reformed, a process—referred to as "turn-over"—which involves attachment of the protein to a template or former which is believed to be a molecule of ribonucleic acid (RNA). When a protein molecule complexes with RNA it is probable that some or all of the bound ions are released. Release of ions may occur predominantly in localized regions of the protoplasm which are rich in RNA. Such a group of free ions may then attract water from their surroundings to form a small aqueous vesicle containing a con-centrated solution of salt. Such vesicles are a prominent feature of cytoplasm when viewed with the electron microscope.

Transfer of salts from these small vesicles into the central vacuole may occur by periodic fusion of the vesicles with the vacuole. According to this view, a carrier mechanism does not operate across the tonoplast, although the vacuolar membrane contributes to the overall resistance of the cytoplasm to movement of ions across it.

The suggested hypothesis has some features in common with other proposed mechanisms of salt absorption. The mechanism suggested by Goldacre and Lorch (Figure 12d, p. 43) for example, also depends on the ion-binding capacity of proteins, and Bennett (Fig. 12e) proposed that membrane flow and vesiculation may be involved in transferring bound salts into and through cytoplasm. Steward (Fig. 31a, p. 87) has pointed out that nucleic acids may be linked to salt absorption through their function in protein synthesis. Robertson (1951) suggested that mitochondria might transfer ions into the central vacuole of a parenchyma cell, by bursting at the vacuolar boundary in just the same way that vesicles are thought to do in the hypothesis outlined above.

The best evidence supporting the view that salt absorption is linked to protein turnover, other than by a common dependence on respiratory energy, comes from the observation that when protein synthesis and turnover are inhibited with chloramphenicol, accumu-lation also stops, without respiration necessarily being affected. This substance may exert its effects at the stage when the protein-nucleic acid complex is formed and ions are released into the cytoplasmic vesicles. The inhibitory effects of ultra-violet light and ribonuclease on salt uptake can be attributed to destruction of RNA with consequent failure of proteins to release their bound ions.

Further information is needed about the precise mode of action of chloramphenicol in preventing protein synthesis and salt absorption before the above suggestion can be accepted with confidence. The validity of the overall hypothesis depends on the ability of enzymes (or other proteins) from plant cells to combine with ions with a specificity comparable to that exhibited by salt absorption, and on the assumption that bound ions are released when proteins complex with RNA. Experimental techniques through which these possibilities may be examined, are being investigated.

Consideration of the salt relations of intact vascular plants introduces a further level of complexity arising from the anatomy of tissues and organs. Some salt is apparently carried passively across the root cortex into the stele with the transpiration stream via cell walls. Active mechanisms are however also involved, and are often of paramount importance, as is indicated by the high concentration of salt frequently found in xylem sap, and by the selectivity of salt transport from the medium into shoots. Active transport of salts into the conducting elements of the xylem has much in common with that of accumulation in vacuoles of parenchyma, and a greater understanding of the latter will surely clarify our knowledge of the former. The mechanism of movement of salts over relatively long distances through the cytoplasm of unspecialized parenchyma is not yet understood, but protoplasmic streaming may play some part in transport of ions bound to protein, and small cytoplasmic vesicles containing salt may move from cell to cell via the protoplasmic connections.

The primary distribution of salts in the stele takes place by mass flow in the transpiration stream, and individual organs of the shoot thus initially receive a supply of nutrients, in proportion to the amount of water absorbed. Subsequent redistribution takes place mainly in the phloem towards the regions of active growth. The remarkable ability of growing cells to attract solutes seems to be linked with a capacity to extract water and nutrients from the sieve tubes, and may well depend on the intensity of protein synthesis or turnover.

Early enquirers embarked upon studies of salt absorption and transport in the belief that these processes could be explained largely without reference to other plant activities. It is now clear that to explain what seems to be a specific aspect of plant physiology one has almost to understand life itself. Thus the mechanism of an apparently simple function such as salt absorption proves to be immensely complex, and may tax the ultimate limits of our understanding.

O Lord, how wonderful are Thy works,
and Thy thoughts are very deep.

REFERENCES

(Figures in brackets indicate pages in the text where the reference is mentioned.)

ADRIANI, M. J. (1958). Halophyten. *Encycl. Plant Physiol.* IV, 709–36. (156, Fig. 48).

ALBERDA, T. (1948). The influence of some external factors on growh andt phosphate uptake of maize plants of different salt conditions. *Rec. Trav. Bot. Néerl.* **41**, 541–601. (49, Fig. 15a; 69, Fig. 24b).

ANDERSSEN, F. G. (1929). Some seasonal changes in the tracheal sap of pear and apricot trees. *Plant Physiol.* **4**, 459–76. (124).

ARENS, K. (1936). Physiologisch-polarisierter Massenaustausch und Photosynthese bei submersen Wasserpflanzen. II. Die Ca(HCO₃)₂-Assimiliation. *Jb. Wiss. Bot.* **83**, 513–60. (21; 50).

ARISZ, W. H. (1945). Contribution to a theory on the absorption of salts by the plant, and their transport in parenchymatous tissue. *Proc. Kon. Ak. Wetensch. Amsterdam* **48**, 420–46. (28).

ARISZ, W. H. (1952). Transport of organic compounds. *Ann. Rev. Plant Physiol.* **3**, 109–30. (133).

ARISZ, W. H. (1953). Active uptake, vacuole secretion, and plasmatic transport of chloride ions in leaves of *Vallisneria spiralis*. *Acta. Bot. Néerl.* **1**, 506–15. (21; 100; 108; 109; Fig. 37).

ARISZ, W. H. (1958). Influence of inhibitors on the uptake and the transport of chloride ions in leaves of *Vallisneria spiralis*. *Acta. Bot. Néerl.* **7**, 1–32. (110).

ARISZ, W. H., CAMPHIUS, I. J., HEIKENS, H. and TOOREN, A. J. van. (1955). The secretion of the salt glands of *Limonium latifolium* Ktze. *Acta. Bot. Néerl.* **4**, 322–38. (161).

ARISZ, W. H. and SCHREUDER, M. J. (1956). The path of salt transport in *Vallisneria* leaves. *Proc. Kon. Ak. Wetensch. Amsterdam* **59**, 454–60. (63; 108).

ARISZ, W. H. and SOL, H. H. (1956). Influence of light and sucrose on the uptake and transport of chloride in *Vallisneria* leaves. *Acta. Bot. Néerl.* **5**, 218–46. (108).

ARNON, D. I. (1955). The chloroplast as a complete photosynthetic unit. *Science*, **122**, 9–16. (108).

ARNON, D. I., FRATZKE, W. E. and JOHNSON, C. M. (1942). Hydrogen ion concentration in relation to absorption of inorganic nutrients by higher plants. *Plant Physiol.* **17**, 515–24. (55).

ARNON, D. I. and HOAGLAND, D. R. (1943). Composition of the tomato plant as influenced by nutrient supply in relation to fruiting. *Bot. Gaz.* **104**, 576–90. (126).

ARNON, D. I., STOUT, P. R. and SIPOS, F. (1940). Radioactive phosphorus as an indicator of phosphorus absorption of tomato plants at various stages of development. *Amer. J. Bot.* **27**, 791–98. (122).

BANGE, G. G. J. (1959). Interactions in the potassium and sodium absorption by intact maize seedlings. *Plant and Soil*, **11**, 17–40. (60).

BARTLEY, W. and DAVIES, R. E. (1954). Active transport of ions by subcellular particles. *Biochem. Journ.* **57**, 37–49. (107).

BECKING, J. H. (1956). On the mechanism of ammonium ion uptake by maize roots. *Acta. Bot. Néerl.* **5**, 1–79. (26).

BENNET-CLARK, T. A. (1956). Salt accumulation and mode of action of auxin. A preliminary hypothesis. *The Chemistry and Mode of Action of Plant Growth Substances* (Ed. R. L. Wain and F. Wightman.) (pp. 284–91.) Butterworths, London. (87, Fig. 31b).

BENNET-CLARK, T. A. and BEXON, D. (1946). Water relations of plant cells. IV. Diffusion effects observed in plasmolysed tissues. *New Phytologist*, **45**, 5–17. (104).

BENNETT, H. S. (1956). The concept of membrane flow and membrane vesiculation as mechanisms for active transport and ion pumping. *J. Biophys. Biochem. Cytol.* **2**, Part **4**, 99–103. (43, Fig. 12e, 106).

BERNSTEIN, L. and AYERS, A. D. (1953). Salt tolerance of five varieties of carrot. *Proc. Amer. Soc. Hort. Sci.* **61**, 360–66. (152).

BERNSTEIN, L. and HAYWARD, H. E. (1958). Physiology of salt tolerance. *Ann. Rev. Plant Physiol.* **9**, 25–46. (151, Table 16).

BERRY, W. E. and STEWARD, F. C. (1934). The absorption and accumulation of solutes by living plant cells. VI. The absorption of potassium bromide from dilute solutions by tissue from various plant storage organs. *Ann. Bot. Lond.* **48**, 395–410. (77, Fig. 27).

BERTRAND, G. and PERIETZEANU, D. J. (1927). Sur les proportions relatives de potassium et de sodium chez les plantes. *C.R. Acad. Sci. Paris*, **184**, 1616–18. (153, Table 17a).

BIDDULPH, O. (1941). Diurnal migration of injected radio-phosphorus from bean leaves. *Amer. Journ. Bot.* **28**, 348–52. (132).

BIDDULPH, O. (1951). The translocation of minerals in plants. *Mineral Nutrition of Plants* (Ed. E. Truog). (pp. 261–75). University of Wisconsin Press. (125; 126, Fig. 42; 128; 129, Fig. 44a).

BIDDULPH, O. (1959). Translocation of inorganic solutes. *Plant Physiology. A Treatise* (Ed. F. C. Steward), Vol. II, Chap. 6, pp. 553–603, Academic Press, New York. (132).

BIDDULPH, O., BIDDULPH, S., CORY, R. A. and KOONTZ, H. B. (1958). Circulation patterns for P^{32}, S^{35} and Ca^{45} in the bean plant. *Plant Physiol.* **33**, 293–300. (128).

BIDDULPH, O. and MARKLE, J. (1944). Translocation of radiophosphorus in the phloem of the cotton plant. *Amer. J. Bot.* **31**, 65–70. (132).

BOLLARD, E. G. (1953). The use of tracheal sap in the study of apple tree nutrition. *J. Exp. Bot.* **4**, 363–68. (124; 125, Fig. 41).

BOLLARD, E. G. (1957). Translocation of organic nitrogen in the xylem. *Aust. J. Biol. Sci.* **10**, 292–301. (124).

BRIGGS, G. E. (1932). The absorption of salts by plant tissues considered as ionic exchange. *Ann. Bot. Lond.* **46**, 301–22. (75; 95).

BRIGGS, G. E., HOPE, A. B. and PITMAN, M. G. (1958). Exchangeable ions in beet disks at low temperature. *J. Exp. Bot.* **9**, 128–41. (100).

BRIGGS, G. E. and PITMAN, M. G. (1959). Unpublished data. (103).

BRIGGS, G. E. and ROBERTSON, R. N. (1957). Apparent free space. *Ann. Rev. Plant Physiol.* **8**, 11–30. (99).

BRÖNSTED, J. N. (1937). *Physical Chemistry* (Translated by R. P. Bell.) Heinemann, London. (34).

BROOKS, S. C. (1929). The accumulation of ions in living cells–a non-equilibrium condition. *Protoplasma*, **8**, 389–412. (74).

BROOKS, S. C. (1940). The intake of radioactive isotopes by living cells. *Cold Spring Harbor Symp. Quant. Biol.* **8**, 171–80. (95; 96, Fig. 34a).

BROUWER, R. (1954). The regulating influence of transpiration and suction tension on the water and salt uptake by roots of intact *Vicia faba* plants. *Acta Bot. Néerl.* **3**, 264–312. (63; 112; 116).

BROUWER, R. (1956). Investigations into the occurrence of active and passive components in the ion uptake by *Vicia faba*. *Acta Bot. Néerl.* **5**, 287–314. (116).

BROYER, T. C. (1950). Further observations on the absorption and translocation of inorganic solutes using radioactive isotopes with plants. *Plant Physiol.* **25**, 367–76. (119).

BROYER, T. C. and HOAGLAND, D. R. (1943). Metabolic activities of roots and their bearing on the relation of upward movement of salts and water in plants. *Amer. Journ. Bot.* **30**, 261–73. (113; 115, Table 9).

BROYER, T. C. and OVERSTREET, R. (1940). Cation exchange in plant roots in relation to metabolic factors. *Amer. Journ. Bot.* **27**, 425–30. (101).

BULL, H. B. (1951). *Physical Biochemistry* (2nd Ed.) Wiley, New York. (29).

BURD, J. S. and MARTIN, J. C. (1924). Secular and seasonal changes in the soil solution. *Soil Sci.* **18**, 151–67. (136; 137, Table 13a).

BUTLER, G. W. (1953). Ion uptake by young wheat plants. II. The "apparent free space" of wheat roots. *Physiol. Plant.* **6**, 617–35. (100, 118).

BUVAT, R. (1958). Recherches sur les infrastructures du cytoplasme dans les cellules du méristème apical, des ébauches foliares et des feuilles développées d'Elodea Canadensis. *Ann. Sci. Nat.* 11e Sér. **19**, 121–162. (105; 106).

CHAMBERS, R. and HÖFLER, K. (1931). Micrurgical studies on the tonoplast of *Allium cepa*. *Protoplasma*, **12**, 338–55. (21).

CHANG, H. T. and LOOMIS, W. E. (1945). Effect of carbon dioxide on absorption of water and nutrients by roots. *Plant Physiol.* **20**, 221–32. (52).

CLEMENTS, H. F. and ENGARD, C. J. (1938). Upward movement of inorganic solutes as affected by a girdle. *Plant Physiol.* **13**, 103–22. (122).

COLLANDER, R. (1941). Selective absorption of cations by higher plants. *Plant Physiol.* **16**, 691–720. (60; 70, Fig. 25).

COLLANDER, R. (1942). Die Elektrolyt-Permeabilität und Salz-Akkumulation pflanzlicher Zellen. *Tabul. Biol. Hague* **19**, 313–33. (5, Table 4).

COMAR, C. L. (1955). *Radioactive Isotopes in Biology and Agriculture*. McGraw-Hill, New York. (25).

COMMONER, B. and MAZIA, D. (1942). The mechanism of auxin action. *Plant Physiol.* **17**, 682–85. (64, Fig. 21b).

CONWAY, E. J. (1953). *The Biochemistry of Gastric Secretion.* Thomas, Springfield, Ill. (84).

CONWAY, E. J. (1955). Evidence for a redox pump in the active transport of cations. *Int. Rev. Cytol.* **4**, 377–96. (60, 84).

CONWAY, E. J. and DOWNEY, M. (1950). An outer metabolic region of the yeast cell. *Biochem. Journ.* **47**, 347–55. (97).

COWIE, D. B., BOLTON, E. T. and SANDS, M. K. (1950). Sulfur metabolism in *Escherichia coli.* I. Sulfate metabolism of normal and mutant cells. *Journ. Bact.* **60**, 233–48. (98).

COWIE, D. B., ROBERTS, R. B. and ROBERTS, I. Z. (1949). Potassium metabolism in *Escherichia coli.* I. Permeability to sodium and potassium ions. *J. Cell. Comp. Physiol.* **34**, 243–58. (75, 97).

CRAFTS, A. S. (1933). Sulfuric acid as a penetrating agent in arsenical sprays for weed control. *Hilgardia,* **8**, 125–47. (131).

CRAFTS, A. S. (1951). Movement of assimilates, viruses, growth regulators and chemical indicators in plants. *Bot. Rev.* **17**, 203–84. (133).

CRAFTS, A. S. and BROYER, T. C. (1938). Migration of salts and water into xylem of the roots of higher plants. *Amer. Journ. Bot.* **25**, 529–35. (119).

DAINTY, J. and HOPE, A. B. (1959). Ionic relations of cells of *Chara australis.* I. Ion exchange in the cell wall. *Aust. Journ. Biol. Sci.* **12**, 395–411. (100).

DANIELLI, J. F. (1954). Morphological and molecular aspects of active transport. *Symp. Soc. Exp. Biol.* **8**, 502–16. (30).

DAVIES, R. E. and WILKINS, M. J. (1951). The use of a doubly-labelled salt ($K^{42} Br^{82}$) in the study of salt uptake by plant tissues. *Proc. Isotopes Techn. Conf., Oxford. Radioisotope Techniques,* **I**, 1–8. (25).

DAVSON, H. and DANIELLI, J. F. (1943). *The Permeability of Natural Membranes,* Cambridge University Press. (31, Fig. 6a; 105, Fig. 36).

DEAN, L. A. and FRIED, M. (1953). Soil-plant relationships in the phosphorus nutrition of plants. *Agronomy IV* (Ed. W. H. Pierre and A. G. Norman.) (Chap. 2, pp. 43–58). Academic Press, New York. (69, Fig. 24a).

DEAN, L. A. and RUBINS, E. J. (1947). Anion exchange in soils. I. Exchangeable phosphorus and the anion-exchange capacity. *Soil Sci.* **63**, 377–87. (140).

DELF, E. M. (1911). Transpiration and behaviour of stomata in halophytes. *Ann. Bot.* **25**, 485–505. (158).

DELF, E. M. (1912). Transpiration in succulent plants. *Ann. Bot.* **26**, 411–42. (158).

DEVAUX, H. (1916). Action rapide des solutions salines sur les plantes vivantes: déplacement reversible d'une partie des substances basiques contenues dans la plante. *C.R. Acad. Sci. Paris,* **162**, 561–63. (142).

DIAMOND, J. M. and SOLOMON, A. K. (1959). Intracellular potassium compartments in *Nitella axillaris. Journ. Gen. Physiol.* **42**, 1105–21. (102, Fig. 35b; 108).

DRAKE, M., SIELING, D. H. and SCARSETH, G. H. (1941). Calcium-boron ratio as an important factor in controlling the boron starvation of plants. *Journ. Amer. Soc. Agron.* **33**, 454–62. (146).

DRAKE, M., VENGRIS, J. and COLBY, W. G. (1951). Cation-exchange capacity of plant roots. *Soil Sci.* **72**, 139–47. (144, Table 15).

EATON, F. M. and JOHAM, H. E. (1944). Sugar movement to roots, mineral uptake, and the growth cycle of the cotton plant. *Plant Physiol.* **19**. 507–18. (67).

EIJK, M. van. (1939). Analyse der Wirkung des NaCl auf die Entwicklung, Sukkulenz und Transpiration bei *Salicornia herbacea* sowie Untersuchungen über den Einfluss der Salzaufnahme auf die Wurzelatmung bei *Aster tripolium. Rec. Trav. Bot. Néerl.* **36**, 559–657. (159, Table 18).

ELGABALY, M. M., JENNY, H. and OVERSTREET, R. (1943). Effect of type of clay mineral on the uptake of zinc and potassium by barley roots. *Soil Sci.* **55**, 257–63. (142).

EPSTEIN, E. (1954). Cation-induced respiration in barley roots. *Science*, **120**, 987–8. (82).

EPSTEIN, E. (1955). Passive permeation and active transport of ions in plant roots. *Plant Physiol.* **30**, 529–35. (98, 118).

EPSTEIN, E. and HAGEN, C. E. (1952). A kinetic study of the absorption of alkali cations by barley roots. *Plant Physiol.* **27**, 457–74. (55, 56, Fig. 18a; 59, Fig. 19; 60).

EPSTEIN, E. and LEGGETT, J. E. (1954). The absorption of alkaline earth cations by barley roots: kinetics and mechanism. *Amer. Journ. Bot.* **41**, 785–91. (60).

ESAU, K. (1953). *Plant Anatomy*, Wiley, New York. (15, Fig. 3a).

ESAU, K., CURRIER, H. B. and CHEADLE, V. I. (1957). Physiology of phloem. *Ann. Rev. Plant Physiol.* **8**, 349–74. (133).

FAWZY, H., OVERSTREET, R. and JACOBSON, L. (1954). The influence of hydrogen ion concentration on cation absorption by barley roots. *Plant Physiol.* **29**, 234–37. (62).

FOGG, G. E. (1947). Quantitative studies on the wetting of leaves by water. *Proc. Roy. Soc.* B. **134**, 503–22. (131).

FREY-WYSSLING, A. (1945). *Ernährung und Stoffwechsel der Pflanzen.* Buchergilde, Gutenberg, Zürich. (145, Fig. 46).

FREY-WYSSLING, A. (1952). Growth of plant cell walls. *Symp. Soc. Exp. Biol.* **6**, 320–28. (104).

FRIED, M. and NOGGLE, J. C. (1958). Multiple site uptake of individual cations by roots as affected by hydrogen ions. *Plant Physiol.* **33**, 139–44. (60).

GAUCH, H. G. and WADLEIGH, C. H. (1944). Effects of high salt concentrations on the growth of bean plants. *Bot. Gaz.* **105**, 379–87. (150).

GLOVER, J. (1956). Methods involving labelled atoms. *Modern Methods of Plant Analysis* (Ed. K. Paech and M. V. Tracy.) Vol. I. (pp. 325–74). (Springer, Berlin). (25).

GOLDACRE, R. J. and LORCH, I. J. (1950). Folding and unfolding of protein molecules in relation to protoplasmic streaming, amoeboid movement and osmotic work. *Nature*, **166**, 497–99. (43, Fig. 12d; 89).

GOURLEY, D. R. H. (1952). The role of adenosine triphosphate in the transport of phosphate in the human erythrocyte. *Arch. Biochem.* **40**, 1–12. (86).

HAGEN, C. E. and HOPKINS, H. T. (1955). Ionic species in orthophosphate absorption by barley roots. *Plant Physiol.* **30**, 193–99. (55).

HARLEY, J. H. and McCREADY, C. C. (1950). The uptake of phosphate by excised mycorrhizal roots of the beech. *New Phytologist*, **49**, 388–97. (21).

HARRIS, J. A. (1934). *The physico-chemical properties of plant saps in relation to phytogeography.* University of Minnesota Press, Minneapolis. (157).

HELDER, R. J. (1952). Analysis of the process of anion uptake of intact maize plants. *Acta Bot. Néerl.* **1**, 361–434. (55, 58, 63).

HILL, T. G. (1908). Observations on the osmotic properties of the root hairs of certain salt marsh plants. *New Phytologist*, **7**, 133–42. (156).

HOAGLAND, D. R. (1944). *Lectures on the Inorganic Nutrition of Plants.* Chronica Botanica, Waltham, Mass. (11, Fig. 2; 117, 142).

HOAGLAND, D. R. and BROYER, T. C. (1936). General nature of the process of salt accumulation by roots with description of experimental methods. *Plant Physiol.* **11**, 471–507. (16, 63, 65, 90).

HOAGLAND, D. R. and BROYER, T. C. (1942). Accumulation of salt and permeability in plant cells. *Journ. Gen. Physiol.* **25**, 865–80. (55, 95).

HOAGLAND, D. R. and DAVIS, A. R. (1923). Further experiments on the absorption of ions by plants including observations on the effects of light. *Journ. Gen. Physiol.* **6**, 47–62. (52).

HOAGLAND, D. R. and STEWARD, F. C. (1939). Metabolism and salt absorption by plants. *Nature*, **143**, 1031–32. (82).

HÖBER, R. (1947). *Physical Chemistry of Cells and Tissues.* Churchill, London. (34).

HÖFLER, K. (1931). Das permeabilitätsproblem und seine atomisch Grundlagen. *Ber. Dtsch. Bot. Ges.* **49**, 79–95. (28).

HOLTER, H. (1959). Pinocytosis. *Int. Rev. Cytol.* **8**, 481–504. (106).

HONERT, T. H. van den (1933). The phosphate absorption by sugar cane. *Verslag* 13e *Bijeenkomst van de Vereeniging van Proefstations-Personeel, Buitenzorg, Java,* 7–20. (26; 54, Fig. 17d; 112; 114, Fig. 39a).

HONERT, T. H. van den, and HOOYMANS, J. J. M. (1955). On the absorption of nitrate by maize in water culture. *Acta Bot. Néerl.* **4**, 376–84. (53; 54, Fig. 17c).

HONERT, T. H. van den, HOOYMANS, J. J. M. and VOLKERS, W. S. (1955). Experiments on the relation between water absorption and mineral uptake by plant roots. *Acta Bot. Néerl.* **4**, 139–55. (113; 114, Fig. 39b).

HOPE, A. B. (1953). Salt uptake by root tissue cytoplasm: the relation between uptake and external concentration. *Aust. J. Biol. Sci.* **6**, 396–409. (96, Fig. 34b; 99).

HOPE, A. B. and STEVENS, P. G. (1952). Electrical potential differences in bean roots and their relation to salt uptake. *Aust. Journ. Sci. Res.* B.**1**, 335–43. (100, 118).

HOPKINS, H. T. (1956). Absorption of ionic species of orthophosphate by barley roots: Effects of 2:4 dinitrophenol and oxygen tension. *Plant Physiol.* **31**, 155–61. (50; 51, Fig. 16b).

HOWARD, A. and PELC, S. R. (1951). Nuclear incorporation of P[32] as demonstrated by autoradiograms. *Exp. Cell Res.* **2**, 178–87. (22).

HUMPHRIES, E. C. (1951). The absorption of ions by excised root systems. II. Observations on roots of barley grown in solutions deficient in phosphorus, nitrogen or potassium. *Journ. Exp. Bot.* 2, 344–79. (88).

HUMPHRIES, E. C. (1956a). Mineral components and ash analysis. *Modern Methods of Plant Analysis* (Ed. K. Paech and M. V. Tracy). Vol. I. (pp. 468–502). Springer, Berlin. (23).

HUMPHRIES, E. C. (1956b). The relation between the rate of nutrient uptake by excised barley roots and their content of sucrose and reducing sugars. *Ann. Bot. Lond.* N.S. 20, 411–17. (67).

HURD, R. G. (1958). The effect of pH and bicarbonate ions on the uptake of salts by disks of red beet. *Journ. Exp. Bot.* 9, 159–74. (52).

HURD, R. G. and SUTCLIFFE, J. F. (1957). An effect of pH on the uptake of salts by plant tissues. *Nature*, 180, 233–35. (52, 53, Fig. 17ab).

HURD-KARRER, A. M. (1935). Factors affecting the absorption of selenium from soil by plants. *J. Agric. Res.* 50, 413–27. (4, Table 3).

HYLMÖ, B. (1953). Transpiration and ion absorption. *Physiol. Plant.* 6, 333–405. (116).

HYLMÖ, B. (1955). Passive components in the ion absorption of the plant. I. The zonal ion and water absorption in Brouwer's experiments. *Physiol. Plant.* 8, 433–49. (116).

HYLMÖ, B. (1958). Passive components in the ion absorption of the plant. II. The zonal water flow, ion passage and pore size in roots of *Vicia Faba*. *Physiol. Plant.* 11, 382–400. (116).

JACOBSON, L. and ORDIN, L. (1954). Organic acid metabolism and ion absorption in roots. *Plant Physiol.* 29, 70–75. (52).

JACOBSON, L. and OVERSTREET, R. (1947). A study of the mechanism of ion absorption by plant roots using radioactive elements. *Amer. Journ. Bot.* 34, 415–20. (76).

JACQUES, A. G. (1938). The kinetics of penetration. XV. The restriction of the cellulose wall. *Journ. Gen. Physiol.* 22, 147–63. (63).

JENNY, H. (1951). Contact phenomena between adsorbents and their significance in plant nutrition. *Mineral Nutrition of Plants* (Ed. E. Truog). (pp. 107–32) University of Wisconsin Press. (145).

JENNY, H. and OVERSTREET, R. (1938). Contact effects between plant roots and soil colloids. *Proc. Nat. Acad. Sci. Wash.* 24, 384–92. (142).

KAMEN, M. D. (1947). *Radioactive Tracers in Biology*. Academic Press, New York. (25).

KAMEN, M. D. and SPIEGELMAN, S. (1948). Studies on the phosphate metabolism of some unicellular organisms. *Cold Spring Harbor Symp. Quant. Biol.* 13, 151–63. (63).

KETCHUM, B. H. (1939). The absorption of phosphate and nitrate by illuminated cultures of *Nitzschia closterium*. *Amer. Journ. Bot.* 26, 399–407. (49, 84).

KNAUS, H. J. and PORTER, J. W. (1954). The absorption of inorganic ions by *Chlorella pyrenoidosa*. *Plant Physiol.* 29, 229–34. (57).

KNIEP, H. (1907). Beiträge zur Keimungs-Physiologie und-Biologie von *Fucus*. *Jb. Wiss. Bot.* 44, 635–724. (155).

KOSTYTSCHEW, S. (1926). *Lehrbuch der Pflanzenphysiologie*. Springer, Berlin. (57).

KRAMER, P. J. (1956). Relative amounts of mineral absorption through various regions of roots. *U.S. Atomic Energy Commission Report* TID-**7512**, 287–95. (113, Fig. 38b).

KRAMER, P. J. (1957). Outer space in plants. Some possible implications of the concept. *Science*, **125**, 633–35. (118).

LATIES, G. C. (1959). The generation of latent-ion-transport capacity. *Proc. nat. Acad. Sci. Wash.* **45**, 163–72. (84).

LEIBOVITZ, J. and KUPERMINTZ, N. (1942). Potassium in bacterial fermentation. *Nature*, **150**, 233. (63; 64, Fig. 21a).

LEPESCHKIN, W. W. (1930). Light and the permeability of protoplasm. *Amer Journ. Bot.* **17**, 953–70. (50).

LESAGE, P. (1890). Recherches expérimentales sur les modifications des feuilles chez les plantes maritimes. *Rev. gén. Bot.* **2**, 55–65. (157).

LEVITT, J. (1957). The significance of "Apparent Free Space" (AFS) in ion absorption. *Physiol. Plant.* **10**, 882–88. (100).

LINEWEAVER, H. and BURK, D. (1934). The determination of enzyme dissociation constants. *Journ. Amer. Chem. Soc.* **56**, 658–66. (45).

LONG, E. M. (1943). The effect of salt additions to the substrate on uptake of water and nutrients by roots of approach-grafted tomato plants. *Amer. Journ. Bot.* **30**, 594–601. (63).

LOUGHMAN, B. C. and RUSSELL, R. S. (1957). The absorption and utilization of phosphate by young barley plants. IV. The initial stages of phosphate metabolism in roots. *Journ. Exp. Bot.* **8**, 280–93. (86).

LOWENHAUPT, B. (1956). The transport of calcium and other cations in submerged aquatics. *Biol. Rev.* **31**, 371–95. (21, 50, 84).

LUND, H. A., VATTER, A. E. and HANSON, J. B. (1958). Biochemical and cytological changes accompanying growth and differentiation in the roots of *Zea mays*. *Journ. Biophys. Biochem. Cytol.* **4**, 87–98. (Plate I facing p. 95)

LUNDEGÅRDH, H. (1939). An electrochemical theory of salt absorption and respiration. *Nature*, **143**, 203–04. (77).

LUNDEGÅRDH, H. (1940). Salt absorption of plants. *Nature*, **145**, 114–15. (82).

LUNDEGÅRDH, H. (1954). Anion respiration. The experimental basis of a theory of absorption, transport and exudation of electrolytes by living cells and tissues. *Symp. Soc. Exp. Biol.* **8**, 262–96. (45, 83, 91, 119, 143).

LUNDEGÅRDH, H. (1955). Mechanisms of absorption, transport, accumulation and secretion of ions. *Ann. Rev. Plant Physiol.* **6**, 1–24. (80).

LUNDEGÅRDH, H. and BURSTRÖM, H. (1933). Untersuchungen über die Salzaufnahme der Pflanzen. III. Quantitative Beziehungen zwischen Atmung und Anionenaufnahme. *Biochem. Z.* **261**, 235–51. (77; 78, Fig. 28a).

MACHLIS, L. (1944). The influence of some respiratory inhibitors and intermediates on respiration and salt accumulation of excised barley roots. *Amer. Journ. Bot.* **31**, 183–92. (64, 92).

MACROBBIE, E. A. C. and DAINTY, J. (1958a). Ion transport in *Nitellopsis obtusa*. *Journ. Gen. Physiol.* **42**, 335–53. (101; 102, Fig. 35a).

MACROBBIE, E. A. C. and DAINTY, J. (1958b). Sodium and potassium distribution and transport in the seaweed, *Rhodymenia palmata* (L). Grev. *Physiol. Plant.* **11**, 782–801. (103).

MASON, T. G. and MASKELL, E. J. (1931). Further studies on transport in the cotton plant. I. Preliminary observations on the transport of phosphorus, potassium and calcium. *Ann. Bot. Lond.* **45**, 125–73. (128).

MEURER, R. (1909). Über die regulatorische Aufnahme anorganischer Stoffe durch die Wurzeln von *Beta vulgaris* und *Daucus carota*. *Jb. Wiss. Bot.* **46**, 503–67. (11, 16).

MIDDLETON, L. J. and RUSSELL, R. S. (1958). The interaction of cations in absorption by plant tissues. *Journ. Exp. Bot.* **9**, 115–27. (61, Fig. 20b).

MILLER, E. C. (1938). *Plant Physiology* (2nd Ed.) McGraw-Hill, New York. (3, Table 2).

MILLER, G. W. and EVANS, H. J. (1956). Inhibition of plant cytochrome oxidase by bicarbonate. *Nature*, **178**, 974–76. (52).

MITCHELL, P. (1954). Transport of phosphate through an osmotic barrier. *Symp. Soc. Exp. Biol.* **8**, 254–61. (97).

MITCHELL, P. (1957). A general theory of membrane transport from studies of bacteria. *Nature*, **180**, 134–36. (88).

MULLAN, D. P. (1931). On the occurrence of glandular hairs (salt glands) on the leaves of some Indian halophytes. *Journ. Indian Bot. Soc.* **10**, 184–89. (159).

MULLINS, L. J. (1940). Radioactive ion distribution in protoplasmic granules. *Proc. Soc. Exp. Biol. N.Y.* **45**, 856–58. (106).

NATHANSON, A. (1904). Über die regulation der Aufnahme anorganischer Salze durch die Krollen von *Dahlia*. *Jb. Wiss. Bot.* **39**, 607–44. (16).

NEWTON, J. D. (1928). The selective absorption of inorganic elements by various crop plants. *Soil Sci.* **26**, 85–91. (70).

OLAND, K. and OPLAND, T. B. (1956). Uptake of magnesium by apple leaves. *Physiol Plant.* **9**, 401–11. (132).

OLSEN, C. (1950). The significance of concentration for the rate of ion absorption by higher plants in water culture. *Physiol. Plant.* **3**, 152–64. (56, Fig. 18b; 57).

OLSEN, C. (1953). The significance of concentration for the rate of ion absorption by higher plants in water culture. IV. The influence of hydrogen ion concentration. *Physiol. Plant.* **6**, 848–58. (52).

ORDIN, L. and JACOBSON, L. (1955). Inhibition of ion absorption and respiration in barley roots. *Plant Physiol.* **30**, 21–27. (92).

OSTERHOUT, W. J. V. (1912). The permeability of protoplasm to ions and the theory of antagonism. *Science*, **35**, 112–13. (152).

OSTERHOUT, W. J. V. (1936). The absorption of electrolytes in large plant cells. *Bot. Rev.* **2**, 283–315. (55, 76).

OSTERHOUT, W. J. V. and STANLEY, W. M. (1932). The accumulation of electrolytes. V. Models showing accumulation and a steady state. *Journ. Gen. Physiol.* **15**, 667–89. (40, Fig. 11b).

OVERSTREET, R., BROYER, T. C., ISAACS, T. L. and DELWICHE, C. C. (1942). Additional studies regarding the cation absorption mechanism of plants in soil. *Amer. Journ. Bot.* **29**, 227–31. (142).

OVERSTREET, R. and JACOBSON, L. (1946). The absorption by roots of rubidium and phosphate ions at extremely small concentrations as revealed by experiments with Rb[86] and P[32] prepared without inert carrier. *Amer. Journ. Bot.* **33**, 107–12. (113, Fig. 38a).

OVERSTREET, R., JACOBSON, L. and HANDLEY, R. (1952). The effect of calcium on the absorption of potassium by barley roots. *Plant Physiol.* **27**, 583–90. (60; 62, Fig. 20cd).

OVERTON, E. (1895). Über die osmotischen Eigenschaftender lebenden Pflanzen und Tierzelle. *Vjschr. Naturf. Ges., Zürich* **40**, 159–201. (10).

PANTANELLI, E. (1915). Über Ionenaufnahme. *Jb. Wiss. Bot.* **56**, 689–773. (11).

PFEFFER, W. (1900). The mechanism of absorption and translocation. *The Physiology of Plants.* (Translated and edited by A. J. Ewart). Vol. 1. (Chap. 4, pp. 86–175.) Oxford University Press. (10).

PHILLIS, E. and MASON, T. G. (1940). The effect of ringing on the upward movement of solutes from the root. *Ann. Bot. Lond.* N.S. **4**, 635–44. (67, 122).

PRIESTLEY, J. H. (1920). Mechanism of root pressure. *New Phytologist,* **19**, 189–200. (15, Fig. 3b; 120).

PULVER, R. and VERZÁR, F. (1940). Connexion between carbohydrate and potassium metabolism in the yeast cell. *Nature,* **145**, 823–24. (63, 65, 75).

REES, W. J. (1949). The salt relations of plant tissues. IV. Some observations on the effect of the preparation of storage tissue on its subsequent absorption of manganese chloride. *Ann. Bot. Lond.* N.S. **13**, 29–51. (16, Fig. 4).

REITEMEIER, R. F. and RICHARDS, L. A. (1944). Reliability of the pressure membrane method for extraction of soil solution. *Soil Sci.* **57**, 119–35. (137, Table 13b).

RICHES, J. P. R. (1948). An introduction to polarographic methods and their application to the analysis of plant material. *New Phytologist,* **47**, 1–16. (24).

ROBERTS, E. A., SOUTHWICK, M. D. and PALMITER, D. H. (1948). A microchemical examination of McIntosh apple leaves showing relationship of cell wall constituents to penetration of spray solutions. *Plant Physiol.* **23**, 557–59. (131).

ROBERTSON, R. N. (1951). Mechanism of absorption and transport of inorganic nutrients in plants. *Ann. Rev. Plant Physiol.* **2**, 1–24. (100, 107).

ROBERTSON, R. N. and TURNER, J. S. (1945). Studies in the metabolism of plant cells. III. The effects of cyanide on the accumulation of potassium chloride and on respiration: the nature of salt respiration. *Aust. Journ. Exp. Biol.* **23**, 63–73. (78, Fig. 28b).

ROBERTSON, R. N. and WILKINS, M. J. (1948). Studies in the metabolism of plant cells. VII. The quantitative relation between salt accumulation and salt respiration. *Aust. Journ. Sci. Res.* B.**1**, 17–37. (80; 81, Fig. 29).

ROBERTSON, R. N., WILKINS, M. J. and HOPE, A. B. (1955). Plant mitochondria and salt accumulation. *Nature,* **175**, 640. (21).

ROBERTSON, R. N., WILKINS, M. J., HOPE, A. B. and NESTEL, L. (1955). Studies in the metabolism of plant cells. X. Respiratory activity and ionic relations of plant mitochondria. *Aust. Journ. Biol. Sci.* **8**, 164–85. (21, 107).

ROBERTSON, R. N., WILKINS, M. J. and WEEKS, D. C. (1951). Studies in the metabolism of plant cells. IX. The effects of 2:4 dinitrophenol on salt accumulation and salt respiration. *Aust. Journ. Sci. Res.* B.**4**, 248–64. (82, Fig. 30).

RODNEY, D. R. (1952). The entrance of nitrogen compounds through the epidermis of apple leaves. *Proc. Amer. Soc. Hort. Sci.* **59**, 99–102. (131).

ROTHSTEIN, A. (1959). Role of the cell membrane in the metabolism of inorganic electrolytes by micro-organisms. *Bact. Rev.* **23**, 175–201. (98).

ROUTIEN, J. B. and DAWSON, R. F. (1943). Some interrelationships of growth, salt absorption, respiration and mycorrhizal development in *Pinus echinata*, Mill. *Amer. Journ. Bot.* **30**, 440–51. (70).

RUHLAND, W. (1909). Zur Frage der Ionenpermeabilität. *Z. Wiss. Bot.* **1**, 747–63. (11).

RUHLAND, W. (1912). Untersuchungen über die Hautdrüsen der Plumbaginaceen. Ein Beitrag zur Biologie der Halophyten. *Jb. Wiss. Bot.* **55**, 409–71. (156; 159; 160, Fig. 50a).

RUSSELL, R. S. (1954). The relationship between metabolism and the accumulation of ions by plants. *Symp. Soc. Exp. Biol.* **8**, 343–66. (81, 84).

RUSSELL, R. S. and MARTIN, R. P. (1953). A study of the absorption and utilization of phosphate by young barley plants. I. The effect of external concentration on the distribution of absorbed phosphate between roots and shoots. *Journ. Exp. Bot.* **4**, 108–27. (119).

RUSSELL, R. S. and SHORROCKS, V. M. (1959). The relationship between transpiration and the absorption of inorganic ions by intact plants. *Journ. Exp. Bot.* **10**, 301–16. (121, Table 12).

SACHS, J. (1875). *Textbook of Botany* (English Ed. Translated by A. W. Bennett and W. T. Thiselton Dyer). Oxford University Press. (10, 141).

SANDSTRÖM, B. (1950). The ion absorption in roots lacking epidermis. *Physiol. Plant.* **3**, 496–505. (118).

SCHATZ, A., CHERONIS, N. D., SCHATZ, V. and TRELAWNY, G. (1954). Chelation (sequestration) as a biological weathering factor in pedogenesis. *Proc. Pa. Acad. Sci.* **28**, 44–51. (70).

SCHIMPER, A. F. W. (1891). *Die Indomalayische Strandflora*, Jena. (157).

SCHMIDT, O. (1936). Die Mineralstoffaufnahme der höheren Pflanze als Funktion einer Wechselbeziehung zwischen inneren und ausseren Faktoren. *Z. Bot.* **30**, 289–334. (115).

SCHTSCHERBAK, J. (1910). Über die Salzausscheidung durch die Blätter von *Statice gmelinii Ber. Dtsch. Bot. Ges.* **28**, 30–34. (161).

SCOTT, F. M. (1950). Internal suberisation of tissues. *Bot. Gaz.* **111**, 378–94. (131).

SCOTT, G. T. (1943). The mineral composition of *Chlorella pyrenoidosa* grown in culture media containing varying concentrations of calcium, magnesium, potassium and sodium. *J. Cell. Comp. Physiol.* **21**, 327–38. (59, 60).

SCOTT, G. T. and HAYWARD, H. R. (1953). Metabolic factors influencing sodium and potassium distribution in *Ulva lactuca*. *Journ. Gen. Physiol.* **36**, 659–71. (49, Fig. 15b, 154).

Scott, G. T. and Hayward, H. R. (1954). Evidence for the presence of separate mechanisms regulating potassium and sodium distribution in *Ulva lactuca*. *Journ. Gen. Physiol.* **37**, 601–20. (154).

Scott, G. T., Voe, R. de, Hayward, H. R. and Craven, G. (1957). Exchange of sodium ions in *Ulva lactuca*. *Science*, **125**, 160. (103).

Skelding, A. D. and Winterbotham, J. (1939). The structure and development of the hydathodes of *Spartina townsendii*, Groves. *New Phytologist*, **38**, 69–79. (160, Fig. 50b).

Sollner, K. (1932). Über Mosaik membranen. *Biochem. Z.* **244**, 370–81. (74).

Sollner, K. (1955). A physico-chemical cell model which simultaneously accumulates anions and cations against concentration gradients. *Arch. Biochem.* **54**, 129–34. (74).

Stahl, E. (1894). Einige Versuche über Transpiration und Assimilation. *Bot. Z.* **52**, 117-45. (158).

Stanbury, S. W. and Mudge, G. H. (1953). Potassium metabolism of liver mitochondria. *Proc. Soc. Exp. Biol. (N.Y.)* **82**, 675–81. (107).

Steemann Nielsen, E. (1951). Passive and active ion transport during photosynthesis in water plants. *Physiol. Plant.* **4**, 189–98. (21, 50).

Steiner, M. (1934). Zur Ökologie der Slazmarschen der nordösterlichen Vereinigten Staaten von Nord-Amerika. *Jb. Wiss. Bot.* **81**, 94–202. (158, Fig. 49a).

Steiner, M. (1939). Die Zusammensetzung des Zellsaftes bie höheren Pflanzen in ihrer ökologischen Bedeutung. *Ergehn Biol.* **17**, 151–254. (157; 158, Fig. 49b).

Steward, F. C. (1937). Salt accumulation by plants—the rôle of growth and metabolism. *Trans. Faraday Soc.* **33**, 1006–16. (16).

Steward, F. C. and Harrison, J. A. (1939). The absorption and accumulation of salts by living plant cells. IX. The absorption of rubidium bromide by potato discs. *Ann. Bot.* N.S. 3, 427–54. (65; 66, Fig. 22a).

Steward, F. C. and Martin, J. C. (1937). The distribution and physiology of *Valonia* at the Dry Tortugas, with special reference to the problem of salt accumulation in plants. *Carnegie Inst. Wash. Publ.* **475**, 89–170. (153, Table 17B).

Steward, F. C. and Millar, F. K. (1954). Salt accumulation in plants: a reconsideration of the role of growth and metabolism. *Symp. Soc. Exp. Biol.* **8**, 367–406. (57; 87, Fig. 31a; 88; 125).

Steward, F. C. and Preston, C. (1941). Effects of pH and the components of bicarbonate and phosphate buffered solutions on the metabolism of potato discs and their ability to absorb ions. *Plant Physiol.* **16**, 481–519. (52).

Steward, F. C., Prevot, P. and Harrison, J. A. (1942). Absorption and accumulation of rubidium bromide by barley plants. Localization in the root of cation accumulation and of transfer to the shoot. *Plant Physiol.* **17**, 411–21. (119).

Steward, F. C. and Shantz, E. M. (1956). The chemical induction of growth in plant tissue cultures. *The Chemistry and Mode of Action of Plant Growth Substances* (Ed. R. L. Wain and F. Wightman). (pp. 165–86). Butterworths, London. (18).

Steward, F. C. and Street, H. E. (1947). The nitrogenous constituents of plants. *Ann. Rev. Biochem.* **16**, 471–502. (88).

STEWARD, F. C. and SUTCLIFFE, J. F. (1959). Plants in relation to inorganic salts. *Plant Physiology*. A Treatise (Ed. F. C. Steward). Vol. II, (pp. 253–478). Academic Press, New York. (68, Fig. 23).

STILES, W. (1924). Permeability. *New Phytologist* **13**, (Reprint). (28).

STILES, W. and KIDD, F. (1919). The influence of external concentration of salts on the position of equilibrium attained in the intake of salts by plant cells. *Proc. Roy. Soc. Lond.* **B.90**, 448–70. (55).

STOUT, P. R. and HOAGLAND, D. R. (1939). Upward and lateral movement of salt in certain plants as indicated by radioactive isotopes of potassium, sodium and phosphorus absorbed by roots. *Amer. Journ. Bot.* **26**, 320–24. (122).

STOUT, P. R. and OVERSTREET, R. (1950). Soil chemistry in relation to inorganic nutrition of plants. *Ann. Rev. Plant Physiol.* **1**, 305–42. (140).

SUTCLIFFE, J. F. (1952). The influence of internal ion concentration on potassium accumulation and salt respiration of red beet root tissue. *Journ. Exp. Bot.* **3**, 59–76. (66, Fig. 22b).

SUTCLIFFE, J. F. (1954a). The absorption of potassium ions by plasmolysed cells. *Journ. Exp. Bot.* **5**, 215–31. (21, 63).

SUTCLIFFE, J. F. (1954b). Cation absorption by non-growing plant cells. *Symp. Soc. Exp. Biol.* **8**, 325–42. (90, 101).

SUTCLIFFE, J. F. (1957). The selective absorption of alkali cations by storage tissues and intact barley plants. *Potassium Symp.* 1956. *Annual Meeting of Board of Technical Advisors, Int. Potash. Inst. Berne*, 1–11. (122).

SUTCLIFFE, J. F. (1959). Salt uptake in plants. *Biol. Rev.* **34**, 159–220. (59; 120, Table 11).

SUTCLIFFE, J. F. (1960). New evidence for a relationship between ion absorption and protein turnover in plant cells. *Nature*, **188**, 294–97. (89, Fig. 32).

SUTCLIFFE, J. F. and HACKETT, D. P. (1957). Efficiency of ion transport in biological systems. *Nature*, **180**, 95–96. (83).

SWANSON, C. P. (1959). Translocation of organic solutes. *Plant Physiology*. A Treatise (Ed. F. C. Steward). Vol. II (pp. 481–551). Academic Press, New York. (133).

TAMM, C. O. (1951). Removal of plant nutrients from tree crowns by rain. *Physiol. Plant.* **4**, 184–88. (133).

TANADA, T. (1955). Effects of ultraviolet radiation and calcium, and their interaction on salt absorption by excised mung bean roots. *Plant Physiol.* **30**, 221–5. (50).

THOMAS, M. D., HENDRICKS, R. H., BRYNER, L. C. and HILL, G. R. (1944). A study of the sulphur metabolism of wheat, barley and corn using radioactive sulphur. *Plant Physiol.* **19**, 227–44. (124).

TIDMORE, J. W. (1930). Phosphate studies in solution cultures. *Soil Sci.* **30**, 13–31. (140).

TOLBERT, E. and WIEBE, H. H. (1955). Phosphorus and sulfur compounds in plant xylem sap. *Plant Physiol.* **30**, 499–504. (124).

TRAUBE, M. (1867). Experimente zur Theorie der Zellbildung und Endosmose. *Arch. Anat. Physiol. Wiss. Med.* **87**, 128–165. (10).

ULRICH, A. (1941). Metabolism of non-volatile organic acids in excised barley roots as related to cation-anion balance during salt accumulation. *Amer. Journ. Bot.* **28,** 526–37. (88, 91).

USSING, H. H. (1949). Transport of ions across cellular membranes. *Physiol. Rev.* **29,** 127–55. (32).

VERVELDE, G. J. (1953). The Donnan-principle in the ionic relations of plant roots. *Plant and Soil,* **4,** 309–22. (35).

VIETS, F. G. (1944). Calcium and other polyvalent cations as accelerators of ion accumulation by excised barley roots. *Plant Physiol.* **19,** 466–80. (60; 61, Fig. 20a).

VLAMIS, J. and DAVIS, A. R. (1944). Effects of oxygen tension on certain physiological responses of rice, barley and tomato. *Plant Physiol.* **19,** 33–51. (50; 51, Fig. 16a).

VREUGDENHIL, D. (1957). On the influence of some environmental factors on the osmotic behaviour of isolated protoplasts of *Allium cepa. Acta Bot. Néerl.* **6,** 472–542. (21).

VRIES, H. de (1871). Sur la perméabilité du protoplasme des betteraves rouges. *Arch. Néerl.* **6,** 117–26. (16, 22).

WHALEY, W. G., MOLLENHAUER, H. H., and LEECH, J. H. (1960). The ultra-structure of the meristematic cell. *Amer. Journ. Bot.* **47,** 401–49. (106).

WHITE, P. R. (1954). *The Cultivation of Animal and Plant Cells.* Thames and Hudson, London. (14).

WIEBE, H. H. and KRAMER, P. J. (1954). Translocation of radioactive isotopes from various regions of roots of barley seedlings. *Plant Physiol.* **29,** 342–48. (111; 112, Table 8).

WIERSUM, L. K. (1948). Transfer of solutes across the young root. *Rec. Trav. Bot. Néerl.* **41,** 1–79. (119).

WILLIAMS, R. F. (1948). The effect of phosphorus supply on the rates of intake of phosphorus and nitrogen and upon certain aspects of phosphorus metabolism in gramineous plants. *Aust. Journ. Sci. Res.* **B.1,** 333–61. (126; 127, Fig. 43).

WIKLANDER, L. (1958). The soil. *Encycl. Plant Physiol.* **IV.** 118–69. (139, Table 14).

WOODWARD, J. (1699). Thoughts and experiments on vegetation. *Phil. Trans.* **21,** 382–98. (1, 2, Table 1).

WRIGHT, K. E. (1939). Transpiration and the absorption of mineral salts. *Plant Physiol.* **14,** 171–74. (116, Table 10).

ZIMMERMAN, M. H. (1960). Transport in the phloem. *Ann. Rev. Plant Physiol.* **11,** 167–90. (133).

SUBJECT INDEX

AUTHOR INDEX

191